Second Edition

WORKBOOK

Robin Peak
Ian Barnes
David Evans
John Lucock

to accompany *An introduction to modern economics*

Longman
London & New York

Longman Group UK Limited,
Longman House, Burnt Mill, Harlow,
Essex CM20 2JE, England
and Associated Companies throughout the world.

*Published in the United States of America
by Longman Publishing Group, New York*

© Longman Group UK Limited 1988, 1991

First edition published 1988
Second edition first published 1991

British Library Cataloguing in Publication Data
PEAK Robin
Workbook to accompany An introduction to modern
economics.
I. Title   II. Barnes, John
III. Lucock, John   IV Evans, David
330

ISBN 0-582-06438-4

Printed and Bound in Great Britain
at the Bath Press, Avon

Contents

Preface
Acknowledgements

1	Nature and scope of economics	1
2	Production	8
3	Demand	14
4	Utility	19
5	Supply	25
6	Equilibrium and disequilibrium	30
7	Resource allocation	36
8	Introduction to welfare economics	43
9	Theory of the firm I	47
10	Theory of the firm II	55
11	Introducing the public sector	62
12	Public goods and externalities	66
13	Financing the public sector	71
14	Issues of public policy	77
15	The determination of wages	82
16	Rewards to factors of production	89
17	Introducing macroeconomics	96
18	National income and employment	103
19	Consumption and investment	112
20	Money I	120
21	Money II	127
22	Money and national income	132
23	Cyclical fluctuations	139
24	Economic growth and development	144
25	Macroeconomic policies	149
26	Unemployment	158
27	Inflation	163
28	Balance of payments and exchange rates	169
29	Trade policy	177
30	The European Community	180
31	Economic inequality	185
32	Multiple-choice exercise: Test 1 microeconomics	192
33	Multiple-choice exercise: Test 2 macroeconomics	198

Preface

This workbook is designed primarily to be used in conjunction with *An introduction to modern economics* by P. Hardwick, B. Khan and J. Langmead. However, it can also be used as an independent study guide. It aims to allow the student to allow and reinforce the economic knowledge gained, as well as test progress. It is equally suitable for use by the student working alone, or with classes and seminar groups.

The book is set out in a consistent format, although on occasions not all types of exercises are included in some chapters. Before moving on to the exercises it may be advisable to read the summary of the main points of the chapter. Each type of exercise has a slightly different purpose. Mix and match is designed to test and reinforce your understanding of key terms. The purpose of the practical exercises is to apply the knowledge and techniques that have been acquired. The short-answer questions will require only a brief response to a simple question. The data response section is designed to give a flavour of the real world. For most students, the essay questions offer the most traditional form of exercise. Finally, the group discussion is designed to develop oral skills and should be particularly helpful to students in more applied courses in areas such as Business Studies. The answer sections at the end of each chapter offer the student an opportunity for self-assessment.

In order to check progress, and give help towards examination preparation, there are multiple-choice questions in Chapters 32 and 33.

Acknowledgements

The publishers are grateful to the following for permission to reproduce copyright material:

Barclays Bank plc for table 25.1; the Controller of Her Majesty's Stationery Office for tables 2.1, 4.2, 7.1, 16.1, 19.2, 20.1, 21.1, 27.1, 28.1, 30.1 and 31.1; the *Financial Times* for two extracts, one entitled, 'Mac attack on Pushkin Square' and 'Price controls preventing an efficient allocation of resources'; © *The Guardian* for figs. 13.1 and 13.2 taken from an article by Victor Keegan; the Halifax Building Society for table 9.1; the Humber Bridge Board for tables 10.1 and 10.2; the International Monetary Fund for table 19.3; the National Consumer Council for table 29.1; the Organisation for Economic Cooperation and Development for tables 5.2, 14.1 and 17.2; Professor Freeman of the Science Policy Research Unit at the University of Sussex for the article entitled, 'Will it be Keynes or Kondratiev?'; © Times Newspapers Limited 1990 for the articles entitled: 'Salaries well above inflation' by David Young (*The Times* 19.4.1990); 'War is no cure for inflation' by Rodney Lord (*The Times* 28.8.1990); 'Soviet Union heads towards a fully convertible rouble' by George Sivell (*The Times* 8.8.1990) and 'Food firms put the squeeze on cut price chain' by Mark Skipworth and Fiona Walsh (*Sunday Times* 17.6.1990).

1 Nature and scope of economics

The basic economic problem facing all economies is that we do not possess sufficient resources (land, labour, capital and enterprise) to satisfy all individual and collective wants. The scarcity of resources therefore forces us to make choices, the most obvious of which is 'what to produce'. If we are using all our resources to the full, then producing more of one good will force us to reduce the output of another. For example, in the 1990's rising demand for consumer durables in the USSR and public pressure for more health and education provision in the UK may force both countries to reduce their defence spending. If this happened, the output of armaments would be reduced in order to release resources to produce more consumer goods and services. The cost of satisfying one set of wants in terms of forgone alternatives is known as *opportunity cost*.

Equilibrium

Economists stress the idea of an *equilibrium* in their analysis. Prices of individual products come to a state of rest after a change of economic forces. A frost destroying coffee bushes in Brazil will cause the price of coffee to rise until a new, and higher, equilibrium level of price is reached. Having said that, economists recognise that continuous changes in economic forces and incomplete information can result in a *disequilibrium* where a balanced stable position is not achieved. This might be said to have happened in the foreign exchange rate market between 1980-85 when the price of the £ sterling fluctuated wildly between \$1.05 and \$2.40.

Deductive and inductive reasoning

General economic principles are formed by two distinct approaches. The first is the *deductive* approach which starts by putting forward a reasonable proposition or theory supported by an appeal to logic. If the reasoning yields a number of predictions or testable hypotheses these can be subjected to empirical (or statistical) testing. The second is the *inductive* approach which involves examining the available statistics in the hope that they will reveal general economic principles. Whichever approach is used, we can never be 100 per cent sure that the theory is correct even if the evidence looks conclusive. Continual testing will give us greater, but never absolute, certainty.

EXERCISES

Exercise 1

Mix and match   In these exercises you are required to match the numbered statement on the right with the correct explanation, description or name on the left.

1. The cost of something in terms of forgone alternatives

2. The study of the behaviour of the economy as a whole.

3. The way in which economists go about the study of their subject matter.

A. Wealth

4. The use of statistical methods to test or derive economic theories.

B. Opportunity cost

C. Pareto efficient

5. Anything which has a market value and can be exchanged for money or goods.

D. Microeconomics

E. Macroeconomics

6. A proposition which seems reasonable to the investigator and based on innate ideas.

F. 'Methodology'

7. Consists of ethical statement about what should or ought to be.

G. Positive economics

H. Normative economics

8. A situation in which it is not possible to make someone better off without making someone else worse off.

I. An 'a priori' theory

J. Econometrics

9. Economic analysis concerned with the behaviour of individual units such as firms and consumers.

10. Consists of statements concerned with what is, was or will be whose validity can be tested against the available evidence.

Exercise 2

Practical exercise   Table 1.1

	Great Britain	
Year	Average increase in weekly earnings (adults 18+)	Average increases in prices
1	12.5%	8.3%
2	13.0	13.4
3	23.3	18.0
4	12.7	11.9
5	10.3	8.6
6	8.4	4.6

Nature and scope of economics

(a) Plot a scatter diagram of the figures in Table 1.1.

(b) If available use an OLS linear regression computer program to determine the line of best fit for the data with the average increase in prices as the *dependent* variable. What is the correlation between the two variables?

(c) The two variables you have plotted show a fairly high degree of correlation. Why would you be reluctant to conclude that price increases are caused by wage and salary increases?

Exercise 3
Short-answer
questions

1. How can the economist test the validity of his theories if he is unable to subject them to controlled laboratory experiment?

2. Why can we never be 100 per cent certain of the truth of any theory in economics?

3. Should an economic theory be discarded just because it is based on an unrealistic assumption?

4. Is leisure an example of a 'free' good?

5. What do you understand by the term 'scarcity'?

6. Will a theory thought to be satisfactory in one period of history continue to be satisfactory in later years?

7. Can we regard human wants for all practical purposes as insatiable?

Exercise 4
Data response

With reference to Table 1.2, on the following page, answer the following questions.

(a) What is the distinction between primary, secondary and tertiary sectors of the economy?

(b) Separate the categories of industry shown in the table into primary, secondary and tertiary sectors and calculate the total number of employees in each sector in 1988.

(c) What are the implications of the decline in employment in manufacturing industry for the UK economy?

(d) What explanations can be given for the trends in employment in the tertiary sector?

(e) Could the UK maintain the living standards of its people with a large tertiary section and little manufacturing industry?

Table 1.2 Analysis of Employees in Employment by Industry (figures in thousands)

	1878	79	1980	81	82	83	84	85	86	87	88
Agriculture, forestry and fishing	395	380	373	363	358	350	340	341	329	321	313
Coal and coke	313	305	303	389	275	261	238	222	187	157	135
Extraction of mineral oil and natural gas	15	19	22	24	27	28	30	31	28	26	26
Mineral oil processing	30	30	30	31	26	22	20	18	16	14	12
Other energy and water supply	359	368	371	366	352	338	328	317	308	302	298
Manufacturing	7 281	7 253	6 937	6 222	5 863	5 525	5 409	5 366	5 236	5 157	5 239
Constructing	1 199	1 239	1 243	1 130	1 067	1 044	1 037	1 022	991	1 013	1 045
Distribution, hotels and catering: repairs	4 091	4 257	4 323	4 172	4 138	4 118	4 244	4 342	4 403	4 476	4 627
Transport	1 051	1 056	1 049	987	943	912	908	911	903	903	939
Communication	451	423	437	438	437	433	432	434	437	448	471
Banking, finance, insurance, business services and leasing	1 569	1 647	1 695	1 739	1 798	1 875	1 969	2 083	2 202	2 337	2 528
Pupil administration, national defence and compulsory social security	1 728	1 719	1 667	1 623	1 594	1 606	1 602	1 613	1 619	1 654	1 690
Education and health services	2 834	2 893	2 900	2 908	2 902	2 886	2 900	2 927	2 961	3 023	3 106
Other services	1 509	1 584	1 640	1 600	1 635	1 670	1 781	1 800	1 960	2 049	2 139

Source: National Income Accounts CSO 1989

Exercise 5

Essay questions

1. What do you understand by the term 'opportunity cost' and how is it related to the problem of scarcity?

2. 'Economic goods have prices because they are useful and scarce.' Explain and illustrate.

Exercise 6

Group discussion

Mac attack on Pushkin Square

On January 31st 1990 McDonald's opened a hamburger restaurant in Moscow's Pushkin Square. It has over 15,000 customers a day although the long queues make a mockery of the concept 'fast food'. Litter is no problem as Soviet customers are taking the polystyrene packaging home to re-use. Sales are 'only for roubles' which means the firm makes a mountain of rather useless money.

McDonald's has insisted on employing part-time workers in defiance of all Soviet labour laws. In spite of low wages there were 27,000 applicants to work in the restaurant. All staff have been put through a classic McDonald's brain-washing, exposed to hours of videos of happy smiling staff in western restaurants and have also been put on the full company system of productivity bonus payments.

McDonald's has been forced to set up a totally integrated food supply, processing and distribution operation in the USSR just to ensure satisfactory supply to the restaurant. It has its own experts to supervise right down to the farm level. As a result its own potato yields are 20 to 100 per cent better than on adjoining fields. It sends its own lorries to the farm gate to collect the potatoes as it cannot rely on the Soviet distribution system which traditionally wastes at least 30% of the crop. Milk and meat are given the same treatment.

From an article written by Quentin Pell and Mark Nicholson in the *Financial Times*, 31st January 1990

1. Do you think the Russians are right to allow the symbol of American cultural imperialism into their heartland?

2. Why are the mountain of roubles earned regarded as 'rather useless'?

3. By opening in the USSR McDonalds has had to tackle a hugh difference in business culture, management culture, leisure culture and work ethics. What do these differences consist of?

ANSWERS

Exercise 1

Mix and match   A. 5   B. 1   C. 8   D. 9   E. 2

F. 3   G. 10   H. 7   I. 6   J. 4

Exercise 2

Practical exercise   (a) See graph at Fig. 1.1

Fig. 1.1

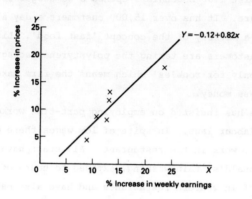

(b) $Y = -0.12 + 0.82X$ where Y = % increase in prices, X = % increase in
wages. Correlation $R = 0.9$.

(c) Both could be caused by another factor such as an increase in the
money supply. Alternatively the wage and salary increases might have
been based on the price increases rather than vice versa.

Exercise 4

Data response   (a) Primary   - extraction of natural resources from land and sea.

Secondary - transforming resources into products.

Tertiary - service industries.

(b) Primary   - Agriculture, foresty, fishing. Coal and coke, extraction
of mineral, oil and natural gas.

Secondary - Manufacturing, construction, energy and water supply.

Tertiary - Distribution, transport, communication, finance and
banking, public administration, education and health.

(c) Benefits

Higher productivity, greater capital investment, service economy.

Problems

Higher level of imported goods, balance of payment problems, regional
unemployment, labour immobility, higher unemployment.

Depends on whether decline in employment is matched by a decline in output in manufacturing industry.

(d) Higher standards of living, greater specialisation, more leisure and better public services may increase employment in tertiary sector.

(e) <u>Unlikely</u>

- Many service industries do not export and therefore would not earn sufficient foreign exchange to pay for imported manufactures.
- Demand for tertiary industry usually directly related to performance of secondary sector.
- Service sector unlikely to generate sufficient employment to replace jobs lost in manufacturing.

Exercise 5

Essay questions

1. Opportunity cost is the cost of anything in terms of forgone alternatives.

The problem of scarcity refers to the inability of any society to satisfy the wants of everybody. Resources are insufficient to produce all we desire. A choice has to be made over what to produce, how to produce them and to whom they should be allocated.

If resources are already being fully used, then a decision to produce more of one good ('guns') will force us to reduce the production of another ('butter'). The opportunity cost of more 'guns' would therefore be the reduction in the amount of 'butter' now available.

2 Production

The range of goods and services we need to produce to satisfy individual and collective wants is large. Individuals will be particularly concerned about acquiring consumer goods (both durable and non-durable), firms concerned about producer goods and the government about defence goods. All three will want services. As society cannot satisfy all wants, it must decide what to produce, how to produce them and 'to whom' they should be given. A *market economy* leaves these decisions to private firms who, in response to public demand and the possibility of profit, buy factors of production and go into production to satisfy wants.

Profit maximisation

Whether firms aim to *maximise profits* is open to question now that many of them consist of large joint stock companies owned by thousands of shareholders who have no say in the day-to-day running of the business. Professional managers are in control and as long as profits are reasonable they may aim to maximise other variables like market share rather than profits.

Growth of firms

Some firms producing new glamour products are likely to experience rapid internal growth as IBM did with computers in the 1950s and 1960s. Others, for reasons of profit, prestige or the elimination of competition, might grow rapidly through mergers or takeovers. *Vertical integration* is when firms in the same industry but at different stages in the production process come together and *horizontal integration* when the combining firms both produce at a similar stage of an industry's production. Increasingly today, however, integration is taking place between firms whose activities are not directly related (conglomerates).

Production

Production is the transformation of factors of production into final goods and services. Therefore the quantity of good X produced per time period (Qx) is a function (f) of the quantities of capital stock (K), labour (L) and land (Ld) used:

$$Qx = f\ (K,L,Ld)$$

To produce more you will need to use more of these factors. However, it is not always easy to expand all factors quickly to increase output. In the short run there is always at least one factor which is fixed. If you wish to increase output in the short run you can only increase the variable factors and this will quickly bring you face to face with the law of *diminishing returns*. This law states that as additional units of a variable factor are added to a given quantity of fixed factor(s) the average and marginal products of the variable factor will eventually decline.

Production

In the long run all factors of production are *variable*. You can therefore *scale up* your level of production by increasing all the inputs of capital, labour and land. Of course, to increase your productive capacity you may not have to increase all three factors by the same amount. The actual combination will depend on factor prices and technical considerations. The firm will have to achieve the right balance of factors to minimise production cost. You may also find that to increase your capacity by 100 per cent you need only increase factor inputs on average by say 80 per cent thus reducing average production costs. This is known as *increasing returns to scale*.

If firms continually add to and upgrade their stock of producer goods, then over time the total output of goods and services in the country will rise. This growth in total output is known as *economic growth*.

EXERCISES

Exercise 1
Mix and match

A. Depreciation

B. Investment

C. Mixed economy

D. Command economy

E. Limited liability

F. Oligopoly

G. Human capital

H. An isoquant

I. An isocost

J. Technological efficiency

K. Decreasing returns to scale

L. Public corporation

M. A firm

1. Some production decisions are left to the market mechanism while others are taken by the government.

2. Where economic processes are determined by a state planning agency which implements the economic goals of society.

3. A decision-making production unit which transforms resources into goods and services.

4. A market dominated by a few firms.

5. The education that is invested in trained labour.

6. The flow of expenditures devoted to increasing or maintaining the capital stock.

7. A situation where it is impossible to obtain a higher level of output with a given level of factor input.

8. A contour line which joins together the different combinations of two factors of production that are just physically able to produce a given quantity of a particular good.

9. A line which illustrates all the combinations of capital and labour that can be bought for a given monetary outlay.

10. The increase in output is less than proportional to the increase in the quantities of factors of production.

11. In the event of a company going bankrupt, shareholders will only lose the amount they have subscribed to the firm's capital.

12. Capital consumption as a result of wear and tear.

13. A form of enterprise completely owned by the state.

Exercise 2

Practical exercise
The following table represents a farm with a fixed acreage of land and shows the changes in total output of sugar beet per year as additional workers are employed.

No. of workers	Total production (tons)	Average production (tons)	Marginal production (tons)
1	10		
2	30		
3	51		
4	72		
5	85		
6	90		
7	84		

(a) Calculate average and marginal production.

(b) At what point do diminishing returns set in?

(c) If the farmer could sell sugar beet at a fixed price of £500 per ton and his only cost of production was wages paid to his workforce, how many persons would he employ to maximise his profits if he had to pay each of his workforce £5,000 per year?

Exercise 3

Short-answer questions

1. Which factors of production are likely to be variable in the short run and why?

2. Why are isoquants concave to the origin?

3. Why is it not possible for isoquants to intersect?

4. Calculate net investment for the year from the following figures (in £m.):

   Capital stock at end of year   50,000

   Capital consumption for year   1,000

   Gross investment for the year   6,000

5. What motivates firms to grow rapidly?

6. List the various costs which make up the final price the consumer pays for a car.

7. What barriers could prevent new firms from entering an industry?

Production

8. What is meant by 'the divorce between ownership and control' in modern western economies?

Exercise 4

Data response

Output per man-hour is one measure of the productivity of labour. The higher it is the greater a country's potential production. In 1981 the Dresdner Bank issued the following statistics for manufacturing, showing that if on average West German workers produce 100 units of output for every hour they work, then workers in:

France produce	83 units
Japan produce	78 units
the UK produce	50 units

(a) What advantages might this give to West German firms and workers?
(b) Give FIVE possible reasons why labour productivity is lower in the UK.

Exercise 5

Essay questions

1. What are the advantages of the principle of division of labour?

2. State the law of diminishing returns and show why it applies not only to land but also to every area of production.

3. What are the advantages of the joint stock form of business and why, if these advantages are significant, do other forms of business survive?

Exercise 6

Group discussion

The Volvo experiment. In the 1970s a number of companies experimented with ways of removing the drudgery and boredom from factory life. It was felt that division of labour pushed to its limit in factories led to low job satisfaction resulting in high absenteeism and poor quality products. Volvo led experiments in the motor industry by developing an alternative way of building cars without the use of the assembly line method pioneered by Henry Ford. Volvo decided that engines and complete cars should be built by small groups of workers who would be responsible for the product from beginning to end. A completely new factory complex was built to accommodate this new method of production. Engines and cars being assembled would move on computer-controlled mechanical trolleys but unlike the old assembly lines the workers would have some control over the speed at which the trolleys move forward. In addition, the trolleys would be stationary while work was being done unlike the continually moving assembly line system.

Production

1. What is to be gained by companies devising ways of improving workers' job satisfaction?

2. Will Volvo's small-group approach increase costs of production over traditional assembly-line methods?

3. Could other ways have been found to reduce drudgery and boredom within the traditional assembly-line system?

ANSWERS

Exercise 1
Mix and match

A. 12   B. 6   C. 1   D. 2   E. 11   F. 4   G. 5

H. 8   I. 9   J. 7   K. 10   L. 13   M. 3

Exercise 2
Practical exercise

(a)

Average production (tons)	Marginal production (tons)
10	10
15	20
17	21
18	21
17	13
15	5
12	-6

(b) When the fifth worker is employed.

(c) 5. It would not be worth employing the sixth person as the extra output would produce less than the annual wage (5 tons x £500 = £2,500).

Exercise 4
Data response

(a) Lower unit costs for firms allowing them to undercut competitors or to make a higher profit. Firms may also pay higher wages and salaries to workers.

(b) Many possible factors. These include:
* lack of capital per worker;
* poorly motivated workforce;
* most talented not applying for jobs in manufacturing;
* inflexible labour force which is reluctant to change;
* poor organisation;
* resentment of authority.

Exercise 5

Essay questions

1. Division of labour refers to the practice of specialisation at work. Illustrated by Adam Smith in his book *Wealth of Nations* with the pin-making example.

Advantages	*Disadvantages*
* higher productivity;	* boredom resulting in loss of quality and absenteeism;
* lower costs of production;	* interdependence.
* increased dexterity of workers;	
* ease of training workforce;	
* capital equipment can be fully used.	

3 Demand

One factor that obviously influences the quantity demanded of a good is the *price of the good itself*. Assuming other factors remain the same (*ceteris paribus*) the quantity demanded of a good usually rises if its price falls (referred to as an expansion of demand) and falls if its price rises (referred to as a contraction of demand). This relationship between demand and price, when presented in the form of a graph, is known as a *demand curve*.

Demand is influenced by other factors such as *size of income*, the *taste of the consumers* and the *prices of other goods*, and over time changes in these factors will cause the demand curve to move its position. For example, in Britain there has been an increase in the demand for 'meals out' in the last 20 years because average real incomes have risen. The demand curve for 'meals out' has therefore moved to the right, indicating that today demand is greater at all levels of price compared with 20 years ago.

Engel's curve

The relationship between income and the quantity demanded of a good when presented graphically is called an *Engel's curve*. Demand for most goods (which we call 'normal') rise when incomes rise but for a few goods (called 'inferior') demand actually falls when people's incomes rise. This is what has happened with potatoes in Western Europe this century.

Elasticity

We know that the quantity demanded of a good alters with changes in its price or people's incomes or the prices of other goods. Calculations of elasticity attempt to estimate exactly how much demand alters when these three factors change.

1. *Price elasticity of demand* measures the responsiveness of the quantity demanded to a change in the price of the good itself. The simplest calculation (*general formula*) is to divide the percentage change in the quantity demanded by the percentage change in price. If a firm knew its product had a price elasticity of 2, it could expect sales to rise by 20 per cent as a result of lowering the price by 10 per cent (thus increasing total revenue). If, however, price elasticity was 0.5, sales would rise by only 5 per cent with a lowered price of 10 per cent (thereby reducing total revenue). A transport pricing policy of high peak-hour fares and low off-peak fares reflects inelastic demand at peak times and elastic demand in off-peak hours, thereby maximising total revenue.

2. *Income elasticity of demand* measures the responsiveness of demand to a change in income. If we buy more of a good as our income rises,

the income elasticity will be positive. This would be true for most goods and services but some, like the new consumer products (video recorders, compact disc players), would have a higher positive value than others. It has often been said that Japan has been more successful as an exporter than Britain in the last 40 years because her range of products has a higher positive degree of income elasticity than those flowing from Britain's factories.

3. *Cross elasticity of demand* measures the responsiveness of the quantity demanded of good X to a change in the price of a related good Y. The demand for butter would obviously decrease if there was a fall in the price of margarine, thus showing a strong positive cross elasticity of demand. This is usual where products are close substitutes. However, a negative cross elasticity characterises complementary goods. For example, the demand for wine is likely to increase if the prices of restaurant meals fall.

EXERCISES

Exercise 1

Mix and match

A. Inferior good

B. Effective demand

C. *ceteris paribus*

D. Engel curve

E. Giffen good

F. Market demand

G. Expansion of demand

H. Price inelastic

I. Price elastic

J. Demand curve

K. Complementary goods

1. An increase in the demand for good X results in an increase in the demand for good Y.

2. Other things being equal.

3. The sum of all the individual's demands for a good in the market.

4. A good whose demand increases as its price rises.

5. A movement down the demand curve.

6. A given percentage change in price gives rise to a smaller percentage change in quantity demanded.

7. A given percentage change in price gives rise to a bigger percentage change in quantity demanded.

8. A good whose demand decreases as income rises.

9. Graph showing the relationship of demand and income.

10. Demand backed up by purchasing power.

11. Graph showing the relationship of demand and price.

Demand

Exercise 2

Practical exercise

Demand for compact disc players	
Price (£)	Quantity demanded ('000 per year)
350	170
300	200
250	250
200	350
150	500

(a) Draw a demand curve of the above figures.

(b) Calculate the (arc) price elasticity of demand when the price falls from £250 to £200 per CD player.

(c) How much extra revenue would be received from the sales of CD players if the price fell from £200 to £150?

(d) Over a two-year period average incomes in the country rise by 2 per cent. The price of CD players remain constant at £250 and sales of these rise from 250,000 in the first year to 265,000 in the second year. Calculate the income elasticity of demand for these players assuming relative prices of goods remain constant and tastes to be unchanged.

Exercise 3

Short-answer questions

1. Is the demand for domestic water price inelastic?

2. Why are potatoes described as an inferior good?

3. Distinguish between inferior goods and Giffen goods.

4. What is meant by product life-cycle?

5. What do you think would be the price and income elasticities of the following goods:

   (a) milk; (b) salt; (c) video recorders; (d) lobsters?

Exercise 4

Data response

Your airline has a daily flight from Humberside airport to Amsterdam. The plane has a capacity of 100 but at the present return fare of £70 only 50 seats on average are sold per flight. Twenty of these passengers can be described as the rich or business traveller and the balance of 30 are tourists. Your sales department has estimated that price elasticity of demand is 0.25 for the first group and 3.0 for the tourist group. The department further suggests the plane should be divided into two classes ... viz a first class with a few little luxuries with fares raised to £84 and a tourist class with no frills with fares of £56. What effect is this suggestion likely to have on (a) the

16

Demand

consumer; (b) the travel agents; (c) the airline; and (d) the airline
caterers?

Exercise 5

Essay questions

1. Outline the factors which determine the price elasticity of demand of
   a product. Does the concept of price elasticity have any relevance
   in analysing the possible effects of a fall in crude oil price in a
   country without its own indigenous supply of oil?

2. In what circumstances can a producer raise his price in order to
   increase total revenue?

3. 'Taxes on alcoholic drink, tobacco and petrol are unfair to
   low-income earners (especially to some old-aged pensioners who have
   smoked all their lives, like the occasional drink and would like to
   run a car to be more mobile) and should therefore be cut.' Do you
   agree?

Exercise 6

Group discussion

Is it possible to distinguish between an informative advert and a
persuasive one?

ANSWERS

Exercise 1

Mix and match

| A. 8 | B. 10 | C. 2 | D. 9 | E. 4 | F. 3 |
| G. 5 | H. 6 | I. 7 | J. 11 | K. 1 | |

Exercise 2

Practical exercise   (a) See graph at Fig. 3.1   (b) 1.5

Fig. 3.1

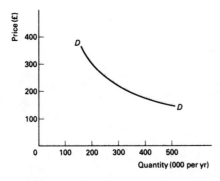

(c) £5 million   (d) 3.0

Demand

Exercise 4

Data response

Enhanced revenue of airline:

(a) Present income per flight (50 passengers x £70) = £3,500.

(b) Future income per flight:

- business

  20% rise of fare will cause fall of 5% passengers

  therefore passengers fall to 19 each paying £84 bringing in £1,596 revenue.

- tourists

  20% fall of fare will cause rise of 60% passengers

  therefore rise to 48 each paying £56 bringing in £2,688 revenue.

Total income per flight now (£1,596 + £2,688) = £4,284

therefore revenue risen by £784 per flight.

Exercise 5

Essay questions

1. Factors:

   * whether it is addictive (e.g. cigarettes);

   * whether close substitutes exist (e.g. no close substitute for petrol for immediate use in cars);

   * proportion of a person's income spent on good;

   * whether it is a necessity or luxury.

   Relevance:

   * allows the government to estimate how much the country's oil import bill will fall and what will happen to its oil tax revenues;

   * helps estimate the effects it may have on the demand for cars, coal and gas;

   * lower energy prices leaving more money in people's pockets will boost demand for unrelated goods and services. The extent of this demand and therefore the resulting increase in output will, in part, depend on price elasticity of demand for oil. Incomes at home should rise.

4 Utility

Several approaches have been developed to explain why a person's demand for a good or service is likely to expand when its price falls. They all hinge on the fact that goods and services usually give some degree of satisfaction (called *utility* by economists) to consumers.

The cardinalist approach

Cardinalists believe you can actually express the degree of satisfaction by using numbers. They put forward the hypothesis of *diminishing marginal utility* which states that the extra satisfaction (marginal utility) a person receives from each additional unit consumed of a good or service falls. In other words, the second Mars bar will yield less satisfaction than the first, and the third less than the second etc., etc.

Faced with many potential purchases and prices, the *rational consumer* spends his money so that the last penny spent on all goods and services yields the same degree of utility. Only then will total utility be a maximum. In other words:

$$\frac{\text{Marginal utility of good } X}{\text{Price of good } X} = \frac{\text{MU good } Y}{\text{Price of good } Y} = \frac{\text{MU good } N}{\text{Price of good } N}$$

If now the price of good X were to fall, the last penny spent on it would yield more utility than the last penny spent elsewhere. The consumer would therefore be able to raise his total utility by buying more of good X. Hence the idea, that demand for a good will expand when its price falls.

The ordinalist approach

Ordinalists believe you can rank combinations of goods and services in order of preference and say which combination gives the higher utility, but unlike cardinalists they do not believe that you can measure utility. Their approach centres on indifference curves which are graphs showing the different combinations of two goods (X and Y) which yield the same utility to the consumer. When the consumer's income (budget constraint) and the prices of the two goods are added to an indifference curve map it is possible to see the combination of goods X and Y the consumer can purchase which will maximise his total satisfaction.

Income and substitution effect

The indifference curve approach illustrates clearly that when a good falls in price the consumer will usually buy more of that good for two reasons:

Utility

(a) Because the good has become relatively cheaper and therefore the consumer will substitute this good for the others. This is known as the *substitution effect*;

(b) Because the consumer is made better off now that this good has fallen in price, i.e. real income has risen. He may therefore buy more of the good with the extra income. This is known as the *income effect*.

So in 1986 when petrol prices fell motorists bought more petrol because it became relatively cheaper than other goods (substitution effect) and bought more because their real income had risen (income effect).

EXERCISES

Exercise 1

Mix and match

1. Indicates all the different combinations of two goods which yield the same utility to the consumer.

2. For all consumers of a particular product it is the difference between total willingness to pay and the total amount actually spent on the product during the period in question.

A. Marginal utility

B. Indifference curve

C. Marginal rate of substituion

D. Substitution effect

E. Income effect

F. Consumer surplus

3. The extra benefit or satisfaction from the the consumption of one more unit of a good.

4. Purchasing more of a good because the fall in its price has made the consumer better off.

5. The quantity of one good that must be sacrificed to increase the quantity of another good by one unit without changing the consumer's utility.

6. Purchasing more of a good because its price fall has made it relatively cheaper.

Exercise 2

Practical exercise   With reference to Table 4.1, answer the following questions.   Ms X has a maximum of £8.50 to spend on oranges and apples per month.

(a) How many kilograms of each will she buy if oranges are £1 a kilogram and apples 50 pence a kilogram?

(b) How many kilograms of each will she buy if oranges fall to 50p a kilogram?

(c) What conclusion can we reach about the relationship of quantity demanded and price from the reaction of Ms X to the fall in the price of oranges?

Utility

Table 4.1   Ms X's utility patterns

Oranges		Apples	
Quantity purchased per month (kilos)	Total utility (units)	Quantity purchased per month (kilos	Total utility (units)
1	23	1	32
2	40	2	53
3	52	3	70
4	60	4	84
5	66	5	96
6	70	6	106
7	73	7	114
8	75	8	121
9	76	9	125
10	76	10	127

Exercise 3

Short-answer questions

1. What is meant by disutility?

2. Write down the condition for utility maximisation for N goods.

   MU of good = _____   _____

3. Is total utility with respect to a particular product maximised where marginal utility is zero?

4. Why are indifference curves convex to the origin?

5. Why do indifference curves never intersect?

6. Draw a budget line on an indifference map and then show the effects of an increase:

   (a) in income;

   (b) in the price of one of the goods.

Utility

Exercise 4

Data response

Table 4.2

Percentage of total UK consumers expenditure at current prices

	1976	1987
Food	18.7	13.4
Alcoholic drink	7.7	6.9
Tobacco	4.2	3.0
Clothing and footwear	7.8	7.1
Housing	13.7	15.5
Fuel and power	4.8	4.4
Household goods and services	7.7	6.7
Transport and communications	15.2	17.2
Recreation, entertainment and education	9.3	9.4
Other goods and services	11.0	16.9
	100.0	100.0

Source: *Social Trends*, 1989

(a) Give three possible reasons why the food expenditure figure has fallen.

(b) How might changes in taxation and interest rates affect the figures?

(c) How do you think the figures would differ for an underdeveloped country?

Exercise 5

Essay questions

1. In the UK since 1950 the price of tea in real terms has fallen and so has consumption. Does this refute the theory of consumer behaviour that states that the quantity demanded rises as price falls?

2. 'The amount demanded of a commodity will usually be greater the lower the price, other things unchanged.' Why is this so, and what is the significance of 'other things unchanged'?

3. 'A fall in the price of a product has both an income and a substitution effect.' Explain this statement.

4. Why is water so cheap relative to diamonds when, unlike diamonds, it is necessary to our very existence?

Exercise 6

Group discussion

There has been a serious road accident with many casualties. Three people belonging to blood group O Rhesus negative, an uncommon blood group, are badly injured and require transfusions of an estimated 6 pints of blood each. Unfortunately only 6 pints of blood exist in total. Who do you save?

Mr A - a wealthy businessman, married but without children.

Mrs B - a young housewife with three children.

Utility

        Mr C - a young man who has just finished training as a nuclear
             scientist but with no family.

As a group, review the merits of each case and consider the alternaive
strategies.

ANSWERS

Exercise 1
Mix and match   A. 3   B. 1   C. 5   D. 6   E. 4   F. 2

Exercise 2
Practical exercise

(a) 4 kg oranges and 9 kg apples.

(b) 7 kg oranges and 10 kg apples, or 8 kg oranges and 9 kg apples.

(c) Quantity demanded is likely to rise when the price falls.

Exercise 4
Data response

(a) People may be consuming less. Incomes may have risen. Relative
price may have fallen.

(b) Taxes on alcohol and tobacco may increase percentages spent on these
goods if demand is price inelastic. Rising interest rates will push
up percentage spent on housing.

(c) Much bigger percentage of spending on food. Less on most other goods
and services especially transport, communications, recreation,
education and other services.

Exercise 5
Essay questions

1. Explain what is meant by a demand curve and emphasize it is based on
one particular period of time.

    In 1950, supply and demand for tea would have established an
equilibrium price as shown by P' on Fig. 4.1.

Utility

Fig. 4.1

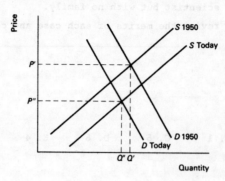

Since 1950 tastes have changed against tea causing a decrease in demand and yet tea plantations have expanded, resulting in an increase in the supply of tea. Both these changes can be seen in Fig. 4.1 and have resulted in a lower equilibrium price today - price P''.

Emphasise that because the demand curve shift is greater than the supply curve shift, consumption clearly falls in the UK from Q' to Q''.

Note that Fig. 4.1 is presented in terms of 1950 prices so as to eliminate the effects of inflation over the years. This is the significance of the phrase 'prices in real terms'.

5 Supply

In a *competitive industry* where there are many firms competing with each other the total quantity of goods supplied to the market is primarily determined by:

(a) The *price of the good itself* - a high market price will not only encourage firms to expand their outputs but might attract new firms into the industry.

(b) The *objectives of the firms* - aiming to maximise sales revenue other than profits will bring forth a greater quantity of supply.

(c) The *price of other goods* - some firms may switch production to an alternative product if its price (and therefore potential profits) is higher.

(d) The *price of factors of production* - if a factor, like labour, becomes too expensive, some firms may no longer be able to compete and will therefore stop producing the good.

(e) *Government taxes and subsidies* - taxes increasing production costs will discourage supply and subsidies will encourage supply.

(f) The *state and application of technology* - new machines or improved production techniques could reduce costs of production resulting in an increased supply.

Search for information

Running a business is not just a question of acquiring factors of production and selling the goods and services produced. Privately owned firms must achieve a satisfactory level of profit which means keeping total costs below sales revenue. Making decisions today which will ensure profits tomorrow is very difficult. If Jaguar cars decide to develop a prestige family car rather than just concentrating on the luxury end of the car market, it must first search for information on the cost and availabililty of labour, raw materials, finance, machinery and then gain more information on market demand to help it decide if the public would buy sufficient quantities of these cars at prices high enough to cover production costs and leave the firm with some profit. With imperfect knowledge and uncertainty about the future, decisions to go ahead with any project must always carry considerable risk. Firms with insufficient information or who interpret the information incorrectly are likely to go bankrupt.

Price elasticity of supply

This measures the extent to which the quantity supplied of a good responds to changes in its price and can be calculated by dividing the percentage change in quantity supplied by the percentage change in price. If the good was unique (like a Picasso painting) or fixed (cup final tickets) the supply is said to be *completely inelastic*. If the supply expands to any quantity required at the same price (like air at zero pence a gasp) the supply is said to be *completely elastic*. Most goods lie somewhere between these two extremes.

Elasticity of supply and time

Time will influence elasticity of supply. At one moment in time it may not be possible to supply any more of the good even if the price rises sky high. The good would therefore be completely inelastic in supply for a few hours. Again, in the *short run*, when it is only possible to raise output by employing more variable factors of production, supply may only rise by a modest amount if the market price rose. For example, no matter how high the price rose Rolls Royce could not increase the output of its luxury cars very much until it had time to extend its factory.

In the *long run*, when all factors of production are variable, supply does respond more to a rise in price. Supply then is likely to be price elastic because there is time to double or treble the capacity of the production unit.

EXERCISES

Exercise 1

Mix and match

A. Price elasticity of supply

B. Industry

C. Short run

D. Market supply of a good

E. Productivity of labour

F. Long run

G. Joint supply

1. The sum of the quantities of a product that the individual firms in an industry are willing and able to offer for sale over a given time period.

2. Output of goods or services per man-hour employed.

3. A group of firms making the same product.

4. An increase in the output of good X results in an increase in the output of good Y.

5. Responsiveness of the quantity supplied of a good to a change in its price.

6. That period of time when all factors of production can be increased.

7. That period of time when at least one factor of production cannot be increased.

Exercise 2

Practical exercise

Table 5.1 Supply schedule of biros

Price (pence)	Quantity supplied ('000 per week)
5	200
10	300
15	500
20	900

(a) Construct a supply curve of the figures in Table 5.1 and read the quantity supplied by firms if the market price was 12 pence.

Supply

(b) Suppose an improvement in technology reduces firms' production costs with the result that firms are now willing to supply 100,000 more biros at each level of price. Draw a new supply curve and read the quantity of biros that would now be supplied if the price was 11 pence.

Exercise 3

Short-answer questions

1. Is domestic water an example of a good which is completely elastic in supply?

2. UK manufacturers deploy far fewer capital assets per employee than in other nations like the USA, West Germany and Japan. What are the problems this situation might give UK firms competing both at home and abroad.

Exercise 4

Data response

Table 5.2 Gross Domestic Product Index (1985 = 100)

	1976	1983	1985	1987	1988
USA	78	91	100	107	111
Japan	67	91	100	107	113
W. Germany	84	95	100	104	108
UK	89	95	100	108	113

Source: *OECD* Quarterly National Accounts, 1989

(a) What do the numbers mean and how are they related to 1985 = 100?

(b) Which of the following statements could be deduced from the figures?

(i)   Japan had the lowest GDP in 1976.

(ii) Japan and the UK had the same GDP in 1988.

(iii) Japan has the fastest growth rate of production.

Give reasons for your answer.

(c) What factors would sustain a high growth rate over a period of years?

Exercise 5

Essay questions

1. Distinguish between 'short run' and 'long run' in economic analysis. Why might one expect the price elasticity of supply of a commodity to be greater in the long run than in the short run.

2. Outline the main factors which determine elasticity of supply. Examine the elasticity of supply of: (a) natural gas and (b) gas cookers.

3. What are the major objectives a private business organisation may pursue? What influences would determine the relative importance of such objectives in a particular firm?

Supply

Exercise 6

Group discussion   *The supply of privately rented accommodation.* You are a management study group of a company which has acquired a block of large Victorian houses in West Kensington (London) designated for residential use only. Your task is to review some of the problems associated with converting the property into flats. Discuss the following issues and prepare a report for the board of directors:

(a) What kind of tenants would you seek?

(b) What kind of tenure will you offer?

(c) The problems of conversion into flats.

(d) The problem of regulation: in particular, the danger of rent freezes, security of tenure and fire regulations.

ANSWERS

Exercise 1

Mix and match   A. 5   B. 3   C. 7   D. 1   E. 2   F. 6

G. 4

Exercise 2

Practical exercise   (a) Approx. 370,000

(b) Approx. 430,000

Fig. 5.1

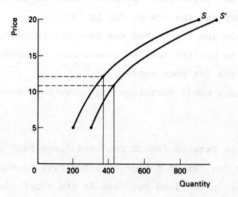

Exercise 4

Data response   (a) The numbers show the percentage changes in each country's production in the four years compared with 1985. GDP in each country in 1985 is represented by the figure 100. As the UK figure for 1987 is given as 108, this means production in 1987 is 8 per cent higher than in 1985. For West Germany you can see that production in 1987 is 4 per cent higher than in 1985.

28

(b) iii) Reason - the total level of production in each country has not been given. The only information given is percentage changes from the base year (1985).

(c) Capital investment in industry, training, labour supply, optimum population, growth in exports.

Exercise 5

Essay questions

1. The *short run* is that period of time when you are unable to change the quantity of at least one factor of production. Costs can therefore be divided into fixed costs and variable costs.

The *long run* is when you have time to change all factors of production and all costs are therefore variable.

Price elasticity of supply is the responsiveness of supply to a change in price.

In the short run it may not be possible to raise total production much even if increased demand pushes up price. Output can only be raised by employing more variable factors. The law of diminishing returns will assert itself and make it financially unattractive to raise output much. In the long run, when all factors are variable, it is possible to double or treble productive capacity without necessarily raising average production costs. Therefore output will be more responsive (elastic) in the long run to a price rise.

6 Equilibrium and disequilibrium

Equilibrium

Equilibrium is a state of rest. In a competitive market the forces of demand and supply will usually ensure that an equilibrium price will be reached where the quantity demanded for each good just equals the quantity supplied. However, with a few goods, market forces are unable to establish this balance of supply and demand. In these cases of unstable equilibrium the market price is likely to diverge from the true equilibrium position.

Changes in price

A change in the equilibrium price of one good can cause a change in the price of another. Higher demand for platinum pushing up its price will encourage mining firms to produce more. This will also increase the production of rhodium, a by-product of platinum mining, causing its market price to fall. In contrast, higher prices of coffee may boost demand for tea, thus causing the equilibrium price of tea to rise also.

Sales tax on equilibrium price

A sales tax on a good is not always passed on entirely to the consumer. Sometimes a portion of the tax is absorbed by the supplier. The more inelastic the demand curve and the more elastic the supply curve the greater will be the share of the sales tax the consumer has to bear.

Disequilibrium

Disequilibrium is a situation where supply and demand are out of balance. The most glaring examples over the years have been caused by government intervention. High minimum prices guaranteed to farmers in the Common Market have led to continuous oversupply. Conversely, low maximum prices for some basic items of food in Eastern European countries before 1989 led to excess demand manifesting itself in long queues at food shops.
  Not all disequilibrium is caused by government action. Demand and supply can often be out of balance because supply takes time to respond to changes in demand. This time-lag is sometimes known as a production lag and can be seen operating with manufactured goods where imperfect information prevents firms gauging the true changes in market demand which their production schedules are trying to meet.

Cobweb model

Disequilibrium caused by production lags can be illustrated by the 'cobweb' model which was originally based on the market for hogs in the USA but can be applied to other agricultural products which have lengthy production lags between the decision to produce and the actual supply arriving on the market. The model starts with the long-run supply and demand for hogs in equilibrium. An outbreak of pig disease reduces the supply of hogs in the current year causing the market price to rise. The high price then encourages farmers to expand output. This extra output

Equilibrium and disequilibrium

increases supply in the following year, causing the price to fall. Farmers then respond by cutting output which therefore reduces supply in year three. Up goes the price again. In this situation price does not necessarily return to the long-run equilibrium position but oscillates around it.

Search theory   Because of imperfect knowledge, all transactions in the market do not take place at equilibrium prices. Firms and consumers have to search for the relevant prices and quantities. For example, prices of the new season's strawberries just coming onto the market will vary considerably. Some sellers might be lucky to sell their supplies at high prices because of consumers' ignorance of prices ruling elsewhere. Gradually, however, consumers will search and find out that other sellers are charging lower prices and will stop paying the higher ones. The sellers of high-priced strawberries will then be forced to lower their prices or be left with unsold supplies.

The analysis of the process of searching for information is known as search theory.

EXERCISES

Exercise 1
Mix and match

1. The price at which the quantity demanded for a good and the quantity supplied of that good are equal.

2. Where a divergence from the equilibrium position sets up forces which do not restore the equilibrium.

A. Maximum price

B. Minimum price

3. Allocating a scarce product or service other than by means of the price mechanism.

C. Jointly supplied goods

D. *Ad valorem* tax

4. A market situation in which either excess demand or excess supply exists.

E. Rationing

5. The production of one good automatically increases the production of another.

F. Disequilibrium

G. Unstable equilibrium

6. A fable where all transactions take place in equilibrium.

H. Equilibrium market price

7. A price floor below which the price cannot legally fall.

I. *Tatonnement* process

8. A price ceiling above which the price cannot legally rise.

9. A percentage charge imposed by governments on the value of a product.

Equilibrium and disequilibrium

Exercise 2

Practical exercise

Table 6.1 Demand and supply schedules for vacuum cleaners per month in a competitive market

Price (£)	Quantity demanded ('000)	Quantity supplied ('000)
20	30	1
40	15	8
60	12	12
80	10	16
100	9	25

Construct a supply/demand diagram of the figures in Table 6.1.

(a) What is the equilibrium price for vacuum cleaners?

(b) What would the new equilibrium price be if demand increased by 5,000 vacuum cleaners at each price per month?

(c) Using the original schedules, what would be the new equilibrium price if the government imposed a specific tax of £10 per vacuum cleaner?

Exercise 3

Short-answer questions

1. Why should a rise in the price of butter put upward pressure on the price of margarine?

2. What is meant by 'search theory' in economics?

3. Why would a government plan to subsidise the production of a good in completely inelastic demand in order to reduce the price and increase consumption of that good be doomed to failure?

4. The Cod Wars between Britain and Iceland in the late 1960s and early 1970s finally resulted in the loss of free access by British trawlers to the rich fishing grounds within a 200 mile radius of Iceland. Draw a supply/demand diagram showing what happened to the price of cod in Britain as a result of the loss of this important fishing ground.

Exercise 4

Data response

Minimum and maximum wage legislation. In 1981 a group of politicians published in their 'Manifesto: A Radical Strategy for Britian's Future' the following objectives for government legislation:

(a) To raise low wages up to a minimum wage, equivalent to two-thirds of average male earnings in the lifetime of a Parliament.

(b) To impose a maximum income limit equivalent to four times the average wage.

Equilibrium and disequilibrium

What are the cases for and against the government implementing these objectives?

Exercise 5

Essay questions

1. Explain, with the aid of supply/demand diagrams, why the prices of agricultural goods tend to fluctuate considerably if sold in competitive markets. What methods could be adopted by governments or international agencies to (a) stabilise agricultural prices; and (b) stablilise the income received by farmers for the sale of their products.

2. What problems can arise if the government attempts to control the prices of particular goods and services?

3. Illustrating your answer with supply and demand diagrams, explain the effect on the market for cars of (a) an increase in the price of steel; and (b) a decrease in the price of petrol.

4. Explain why and how speculators in a market may: (a) increase price fluctuations; and (b) reduce price fluctuations.

5. Examine the tax revenue raised and the impact on consumers and producers when the government imposes a tax on a good with: (a) an elastic demand; and (b) an inelastic demand over the relevant price range.

Exercise 6

Group discussion

1. Do you think the Common Agricultural Policy (CAP) of the European Community benefits both producers and consumers?

2. What problems would be created if it was decided to abandon CAP and return agriculture to the mercy of market forces?

3. Should we charge a levy on firms to make them pay for the social costs of the pollution they actually create (as happens in some parts of West Europe) or is pollution best handled by imposing quantity/quality standards and control with the backing of the law if not adhered to (as in the UK)?

ANSWERS

Exercise 1

Mix and match

A. 8   B. 7   C. 5   D. 9   E. 3   F. 4
G. 2   H. 1   I. 6

Exercise 2

Practical exercise   (a) £60

                    (b) £76

                    (c) £67

Exercise 4

Data response   (a) *Minimum wage*

Case for:

* ensure a good basic living standard for all at work;
* reduces need to pay social security payments;
* will shock some firms into increased efficiency;
* prevent exploitation of workforce by some employers.

Case against:

* jobs destroyed as workers are priced out of labour market;
* encourages the use of machines rather than labour: result unemployment;
* raise production costs thus reducing Britain's competitive position;
* higher paid workers will be unhappy and want differentials restored: this could result in cost push inflation;
* alternative ways of helping poor.

    (b) *Maximum wage*

Case for:

* greater equality;
* very few worth more;
* those who are worth more should want to help society without extra pay.

Case against:

* people will be unwilling to take on high responsibility;
* disincentive to work;
* firms might decide to move abroad and new firms will avoid Britain.

Exercise 5

Essay questions   1. Demand for agricultural goods is inelastic. Any small change in supply will therefore cause a large change in price. A bumper crop will drive price down (see Fig. 6.1).

Fig. 6.1

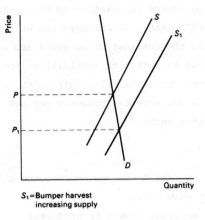

S_1=Bumper harvest
increasing supply

Because there are so many producers of agricultural products it becomes difficult to organise cartels to fix prices (like OPEC with oil). Hence world food market is highly competitive. Protection from this competition seems only possible within one country or a group of countries (e.g. EC).

(a) *Set an intervention price for each product*. If price falls below this target price, the government buys up surplus output and stores it. If price rises, the government sells stock previously accumulated (e.g. EC Common Agricultural Policy).

(b) *Deficiency payments system*. Guarantee farmers a price for every agricultural product sold. If the market price is below this guaranteed price, the government makes up the difference with a payment direct from the Exchequer.

Note Other possibilities include a guaranteed minimum income paid to farmers in return for a fixed quota of output.

7 Resource allocation

With resources being scarce in relation to the wants of society, they must be allocated efficiently to maximise the welfare of the community. This means producing the combination of goods and services that will give the greatest level of satisfaction (utility) to society as a whole. In terms of indifference curve analysis, this point will be reached when the combination of goods and services produced reaches the highest attainable community indifference curve.

System of resource allocation

All societies have to make decisions on resource allocation and the key questions they must answer are:

(a) WHAT goods and services should be produced;

(b) HOW should these goods and services be produced; and

(c) TO WHOM should these goods and services be distributed?

In a *command system* (communism) the state owns the means of production and distribution and sets up a central planning agency to take these decisions. Countries of Eastern Europe, before 1989 and China came nearest to this model. The advantages of this type of system include greater power to control unemployment, inflation and inequality of incomes. However, lack of money (including profit) incentives can reduce the quality and quantity, particularly of consumer goods and services, and state decisions can severely restrict the supply of some goods consumers would dearly like to buy. The USSR found that production and distribution inefficiencies caused shortages of food supplies and state decisions to limit the production of inessential goods resulted in products like jeans and chewing gum fetching very high prices on the 'black market'.

In a *market system* (capitalism), where ownership of resources is in private hands, firms produce what the consumer demands as long as there is a possible profit to be made. Here the forces of demand and supply acting through the price mechanism determines the What, How and For Whom questions. However, countries operating largely through the market system, like the USA, Japan and Western Europe, find the complete textbook conditions of perfect competition unattainable in practice. Lack of information on prices and profits, the monopoly power of big firms and trade unions and the bad external effects of production make this system less attractive than its early advocates, like Adam Smith, suggested. Nevertheless the system does give freedom of choice to consumers and producers; it can ruthlessly promote economic efficiency; and production does respond quickly to changing consumer demands.

Resource allocation

International economy Nations recognise the sense of allowing regions within their own country
to specialise in the goods and services they are best at producing and
then trade with other parts of the same country, but are more reluctant
to pursue a policy which aims for the same advantages between countries.
The advantages of international specialisation and trade can be
illustrated with a two-country model where food and manufactured goods
only are produced. If one country is more efficient at producing food
and the other more efficient at producing manufactured goods (a situation
known as the absolute advantage case), the benefits, through greater
output, of specialisation and trade are obvious. However, these benefits
are not so clear where one country is more efficient at producing both
products. The theory of comparative advantage has been developed to show
that it is relative efficiency that determines whether gains from trade
are possible between countries in this situation. As long as the
opportunity costs of production in the two countries differ and the terms
of trade are such that both countries could gain, specialisation and
trade not only increases total output in the world but increases the
quantity of goods and services in each country (thereby raising average
living standard).

EXERCISES

Exercise 1

Mix and match

1. The relationship between the average price of exports and imports.

2. A commodity or service which if supplied to one person will be made available to others at no extra cost.

A. General equilibrium

B. Community indifference curve

3. Situation when no forces exist to compel buyers and sellers in the markets for all commodities and resources to change their behaviour.

C. Consumer sovereignty

D. Public goods

E. Terms of trade

4. The combination of goods and services that will maximise social welfare on the assumption that the distribution of output among the members of the community remains unchanged.

F. Economic efficiency

5. Indicates all the different combinations of two goods which yield the same utility to a society.

6. Where the decisions as to what to produce are determined by consumers' preferences expressed in the goods and services they try to buy.

Resource allocation

Exercise 2

Practical exercise   Table 7.1   Value of UK exports by destination (£m)

	1974	1984
EC (incl. Greece)	5,457	31,568
Rest of W. Europe	2,624	8,729
North America	2,291	11,406
Japan	321	925
Other developed countries	1,385	3,685
Oil-exporting countries	1,221	5,807
Other developing countries	2,421	7,550
Centrally planned economies	520	1,603
Total trade	16,250	71,299

Source: *Annual Abstract of Statistics*, 1986

(a) Which destination experienced the second biggest percentage rise in value for UK exports between 1974 and 1984 and by how much?

(b) Construct a pie chart for each of the two years. If available, use a relevant computer package such as Lotus 123 to draw the charts.

(c) The value of total trade between 1974 and 1984 has risen by 338 per cent. Does this mean the volume of trade has risen by the same amount?

(d) Are UK patterns of trade determined by political decisions?

Exercise 3

Short-answer   1. What did Adam Smith, in his book *Wealth of Nations*, mean by saying
questions   that individuals pursuing their self-interest would be led 'as by an
                           invisible hand' to do things that are in the interests of society as
                           a whole?

2. Give two examples of goods which cause social costs: (a) while they are being produced; and (b) as they are consumed.

3. Do you agree with Professor E. J. Mishan that further economic growth by the major industrial countries is more likely on balance to reduce rather than increase social welfare?

4. Give four examples of goods that fit into R. Vernon's 'product-cycle' trade model.

5. Why might a less developed country want to:

    (a) reform agriculture;

    (b) subsidise capital and exports;

    (c) license industrial and residential building;

    (d) ration foreign exchange to capital and food imports only?

6. Is the consumer always sovereign in a private enterprise system?

Resource allocation

7. How is the principle of comparative advantage related to division of labour?

Exercise 4

Data response

Price controls preventing an efficient allocation of resources. At a meeting of industrial and agricultural managers in Moscow early in 1985, Mr Mikhail Gorbachev expressed surprise that factories producing old-fashioned consumer products of low technical quality which do not meet the standards the public want still manage to survive and even thrive in the USSR.

The problem of getting products of the right quality and quantity is not merely a question of more money and better organisation. The problem is intimately linked to the prices charged in the shops. If the consumer wants goods of better quality, he or she will have to pay more. Over the last 30 years the prices of staple foodstuffs, accommodation, transport, gas and electricity have been heavily subsidised. The Moscow metro costs 5p to go anywhere, state housing on average costs 3 per cent of individual income and the subsidies on meat, eggs and milk come to £40 bn. (billion) a year alone. In contrast, prices of some consumer goods (like cars) and services are exceptionally high.

With rising real incomes in the USSR and an inefficient agricultural system, supply lags behind demand for many of these cheap subsidised products. Farmers are bridging the gap by cultivating their private plots and growing produce for which they can command exorbitant prices in the 'free' market in towns and villages rather than putting more effort into the state farms on which they work.

The inability to meet the growth in demand over the past 20 years is shown not only by the very high prices on the 'free' market for better quality goods but by the rapid growth of the 'black market'. The black market now meets much of the demand for services. A survey shows that 30 per cent of petrol purchased is bought cheaply on the black market and surprisingly there is often a need to pay doctors for quality medical care which is supposed to be free.

This is a reduced version of an article written by Patrick Cockburn in the *Financial Times* 16/5/85. Since it was written the USSR has adopted *Perestroika* along with the beginnings of reforms to increase the influence of market forces into the economy.

(a) Why did the USSR spend so much money on subsidies?

(b) How is the introduction of realistic prices which reflect the cost of production likely to help the Soviet economy?

Resource allocation

(c) What reforms, in your opinion, will the USSR have to introduce to make the economy more responsive to market forces?

(d) How painful will these reforms be to the country?

Exercise 5

Essay questions

1. What would you regard as the main strengths and weaknesses of the market system?

2. 'Capitalist and communist countries face the same economic problems. It is only the way they solve these problems that differs.' Comment.

3. Is it possible for international trade between two countries to be mutually beneficial if one of them can produce all commodities more cheaply than the other? Give reasons for your answer.

4. What are the main functions of the price mechanism? What factors may hinder the price mechanism from carrying out these functions?

Exercise 6

Group discussion

'State railways should be free.'

'Prices should be charged on state railways but they should be low at all times.'

'State railways should charge high fares at peak travel times and low fares at other times.'

(a) If a choice had to be made between these three pricing policies, consider the pros and cons of each option and decide which one you think the government should adopt and why.

(b) It has been suggested that British Rail should continue to be responsible for track and station maintenance while the actual passenger and freight services are run by private companies. Is this idea both practical and desirable?

ANSWERS

Exercise 1

Mix and match   A. 3   B. 5   C. 6   D. 2   E. 1   F. 4

Exercise 2

Practical exercise   (a) North America recording an increase of 398 per cent.

(b) Relevant percentages for pie charts:

	1974	1984
EC	34	44.5
Rest of West Europe	16	12
North America	14	16
Japan	2	1.5
Other developed countries	9	5
Oil exporting countries	8	8
Other developing countries	14	11
Centrally planned economies	3	2
	100.0	100.0

Fig. 7.1

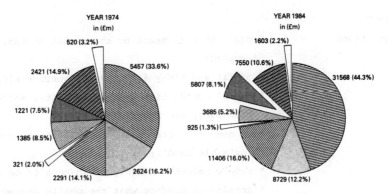

Strictly speaking, the radius of the pie chart should be altered to reflect the much larger *value* of exports in 1984. Value is directly proportional to area of the circle, therefore:

$$\frac{r_2^2}{r_1^2} = \frac{71,299}{16,250} = 4.4.$$

Therefore if r_1 = 1", then r_2 = $\sqrt{4.4}$ = 2.1"
(r refers to the radius of the circle)

(c) No. A large part of the increase reflects rises in prices over the 10-year period.

(d) To a considerable extent. For example, UK membership of the EC has encouraged trade with other EC countries. However, trade with the EEC was becoming increasingly important before the UK became a member and its poor performance in some markets has been due to the inability of UK firms to market reliable goods at competitive prices and not because of political decisions.

Resource allocation

(a) To ensure stable prices of basic necessities.

To ensure that everyone can afford to purchase these basic necessities.

To encourage the use of public transport.

(b) By reducing demand and discouraging waste.

(c) Without this supply there would be severe shortages of some foodstuffs such as fresh vegetables.

(d) Difficult to completely eliminate. State tolerates it because it is not prepared to devote more resources to expand the supply of these goods and services.

1. Explain what is meant by the market system.

Strengths:

* profit and money incentives encourage efficiency;

* firms' competition improves quality, encourages development of technology and keeps prices low;

* no need for bureaucracy to allocate resources (Adam Smith's 'invisible hand');

* supply responds quickly to changes in demand;

* freedom to produce what the public demands.

Weaknesses:

* tends to create inequality of wealth;

* firms tend to amalgamate to restrict competition (monopoly);

* no allowances for public goods and externalities;

* prices of some goods prone to wild fluctuations (e.g. food and materials);

* subject to trade cycles resulting in unemployment during slumps;

* hardship for poor when severe shortages occur (e.g. housing in London);

* workers form unions which can prevent the labour market from working efficiently.

8 Introduction to welfare economics

Welfare economics has grown into a complex body of analysis, and is important in its role in identifying the allocation of resources which is both efficient and equitable. The purpose of the exercise should be to maximise social welfare. This is probably more difficult to do in practice than in theory.

Economic efficiency

Economic efficiency in the Pareto sense can be said to have been achieved when it is not possible to make someone better off without making another worse off. To achieve *Pareto optimality* or Pareto efficiency there must be, first, efficiency in *production*, which means that an economy must employ factors of production so that it operates on the production possibility frontier. Second, there must be efficiency of *exchange* which means that the stock of goods and services cannot be reallocated without reducing the amount available to another. Finally, there must be an efficient *output mix*, which means that the combination of goods and services produced cannot be changed without harming another.

Improving social welfare

Society's *social welfare* can be thought of as being equivalent to the level of satisfaction enjoyed by society. Two main aspects of this are *economic efficiency* and the *equitable distribution* of resources. Pareto efficiency criteria will tell us how to achieve an efficient allocation of resources with very strict rules. Unfortunately it does not say anything about the welfare implications of changes which benefit some, but harm others.

 Equity is a normative concept in that it is based upon value judgements. In order to analyse equity it is still important to have standards to base the analysis on. The *egalitarian* standard aims for greater equality of income and wealth while normally recognising that the incentive to work is important. The *social conscience* standard depends upon the satisfaction that the rich gain from helping the poor. The *underdog standard* sets a poverty line below which the very poorest society should not fall. Finally, the *intergeneration standard* draws attention to the fact that the careless use of resources now may affect the welfare of future generations.

The conflict between efficiency and equity

The problem of judging society's welfare by efficiency and equity criteria is that they often seem to give contradictory answers. An example of this might be the UK government's decision to maintain the loss-making Cornish tin mines on the grounds that if they closed, unemployment might grow worse in an already depressed area. It seems almost inevitable that there will have to be a *trade off* between efficiency and equity.

In order to determine if a policy actually does improve social welfare it has been suggested that *compensation tests* should be applied. This means that even if someone is worse off, it may well be that someone else is better off as a result. If this happens, and if it is possible for the winners to compensate the losers, with a surplus being generated, then social welfare has been improved.

EXERCISES

Exercise 1

Mix and match

A. Theory of second best

B. Edgeworth-Bowley box diagram

C. Bliss point

D. Cost-benefit analysis

E. Contract curve

F. Efficiency in production

G. Production possibility curve

H. Equity

I. Social welfare function

J. Compensation principle

1. A test to see if a policy results in a net improvement in the community's welfare. It is done by comparing the monetary gains and losses and seeing if a surplus results.

2. The analysis of sub-optimal positions to determine the best available positions when constraints prevent an economy from reaching the Pareto optimal position.

3. A device which demonstrates the most efficient allocation of goods between consumers or resources between two producers.

4. The set of points on the Edgeworth-Bowley box diagram which are box diagram Pareto optimal.

5. The point at which inputs are utilised to produce output at the lowest possible cost. That is on the production possibility frontier.

6. Fairness or justice, but not to be confused with equality.

7. The point at which any change in the combination of goods purchased will lead to a loss of utility. The consumers' highest level of satisfaction.

8. A measure of society's satisfaction based upon the utility functions of the individuals in society.

9. The curve which indicates the maximum possible combination of outputs that a society could produce with the resources at hand, assuming no technological advance.

10. Techniques used to evaluate the desirability of investment projects which includes the monetary as well as the non-monetary gains and losses associated with it.

Exercise 2

Practical exercise

Efficiency in production Fig. 8.1 is the production box for the manufacturing of two commodities, televisions (TV) and refrigerators (R).

Fig. 8.1

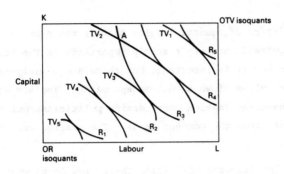

(a) At point A, what is the quantity of televisions and refrigerators
being produced?

(b) Indicate on Fig. 8.1 the amounts of capital and labour required to
produce the refrigerators.

(c) Indicate on Fig. 8.1 the amount of capital and labour required to
produce the televisions.

(d) Mark the contract curve on Fig. 8.1.

Exercise 3

**Short-answer
questions**

1. What is meant by a 2x2x2 model?

2. Illustrate the two ways of writing the social welfare function.

3. At what point on the production possibilities frontier is it
impossible to move without making at least one individual worse off?

4. What is meant by the theory of second best?

5. Why is it true to say there are no real experts on equity in society?

6. Why is it sometimes difficult to reach the bliss point by using taxes
designed to change the distribution of incomes?

Exercise 4

Essay questions

1. Discuss the reason why an apparently simple concept like equity turns
out to be so very difficult to define satisfactorily in practice.

2. Why is it difficult to maximise both efficiency and equity in
society?

3. How might the social welfare function of a developed and a less
developed country differ?

Introduction to welfare economics

4. Why might cost-benefit analysis be a useful technique to judge the desirability of government help to improve the railway infrastructure associated with the Channel Tunnel?

5. Can the maintainance of import quotas on textiles be justified on economic grounds?

Exercise 5

Group discussion

The politics of equity. Imagine that in the next election, the issue of a more equitable society rises in importance on the political agenda. All parties say it is important, but there are clearly differences in the parties' views of what the concept means. You are all taking part in a face-the-press session where senior politicians put forward their view of what they feel the concept means. The session will take the following format.

1. The politicians will state their view as to what equity means. So, for example, you would expect the Green Party's representative to put forward views with a strong intergenerational standard element.

2. The politicians would then be expected to explain to the press how their views differed from the other parties. This would be in response to press questioning.

3. The contribution to society's social welfare should be explained, in particular the implications that the proposals might have for economic efficiency.

ANSWERS

Exercise 1

Mix and match

| A. 2 | B. 3 | C. 7 | D. 10 | E. 4 |
| F. 5 | G. 9 | H. 6 | I. 8 | J. 1 |

Exercise 2

Practical exercise   (a) TV2, R3

Exercise 4

Essay questions

1. * This question hinges on the problem of defining the term equity.
   * It calls for a discussion of a normative rather than a positive issue.
   * The egalitarian, social conscience, underdog and intergeneration standards should be discussed. In particular, the problem of compatibility should be examined.

9 Theory of the firm I

The theory of the firm is concerned with the analysis of firms' output and pricing decisions. The decisions themselves are influenced by the business objectives of the enterprises in question and by the nature of the markets in which they operate. After dealing with the nature of business costs and revenue and their relationship with output, this chapter considers the *profit-maximising goal* in relation to perfectly competitive firms. Other market types and business goals are taken up in Chapter 10.

Costs of production

Economists take a broader view of costs than accountants since they take into account the *opportunity cost* of funds invested in a business. For example, economists would reckon as a cost the sacrificed interest on funds that might alternatively have been loaned out rather than invested in the business.

In the *short-run*, some costs will be of a fixed nature in relation to output - e.g. rent and rates - while others will vary with output - e.g. labour and raw material costs. Labour productivity in the shape of increasing and diminishing returns, plus the existence of fixed factors, critically influence the relationships between the various cost curves and their behaviour against output. U-shaped average total cost curves are typical as, first, the spreading of overheads brings average costs down sharply and subsequently strongly diminishing returns set in to pull average costs up as output increases. The marginal cost curve starts to rise with output once diminishing marginal returns set in, and passes through the bottom of the average cost curves.

In the *long-run*, all factors can be varied and the existence, or otherwise, of economies of scale influences the shape of a firm's long-run average cost curve (LRAC). Internal economies, which can be technical - e.g. assembly line production - or non-technical - e.g. bulk-buying discounts - in nature, cause the LRAC curve to fall as output increases. It is, however, possible that the LRAC curve might start to rise when firms reach a large size owing to diseconomies caused by administrative and organisational problems.

Revenue, costs and profits

A firm's profit is simply its total revenue or sales receipts less its total cost. Average revenue (AR) equals total revenue per unit of output sold for any particular product and, given uniform pricing by firms, AR equals price. Marginal revenue (MR) equals the change in total revenue resulting from a unit increase in output sold. The shapes of the AR and MR curves and the relationship between them depends on the market circumstances which a firm faces. Regardless of these circumstances, profits will be maximised if MR = MC (marginal cost) providing the MC curve cuts the MR curve from below.

Perfect competition

Numerous buyers and sellers, and freedom of entry and exit of firms are two of the more important features characterising perfectly competitive markets.

Any single firm in the market has a very small market share and consequently is a price-taker facing a perfectly elastic demand curve. This means that price (P) = MR so that profit-maximising behaviour ensures that competitive firms practise marginal cost pricing. The marginal cost curve therefore represents the firm's supply curve.

Equilibrium price and output in the market are determined by the forces of supply and demand with the industry supply curve being the horizontal summation of the firms' marginal cost curves.

It is possible in the short-run for firms to earn surplus profits following an increase in market demand which raises the market price of the product. However, these surplus profits are competed away in the long-run as new firms attracted by the profits enter the industry. In the case of a decrease in demand and short-run losses for firms, normal profit would be restored in the long-run, for the surviving firms, by the exit of firms from the industry. The long-run equilibrium position is such that for each firm P=MC=AC, with firms operating at the bottom of their average cost curves.

For an efficient allocation of resources, the marginal rate of substitution (MRS) must equal the marginal rate of transformation (MRT) for all possible pairs of goods. In the absence of market externalities, a perfectly competitive economy would satisfy this equality since all firms set their product prices equal to marginal costs.

EXERCISES

Exercise 1
Mix and match

A. Fixed costs

B. Average total cost

C. Marginal cost

D. Opportunity cost of capital

E. Long-run average cost curve

1. A firm that is unable to exert any influence on market prices by varying its output.

2. The extra cost incurred by a firm when an additional unit of output is produced.

3. Shows the minimum possible unit cost of producing any level of output when all factors are variable.

4. A firm's total receipts from the sale of a product expressed per unit sold.

Theory of the firm I

F. Internal economies of scale

G. Average revenue

H. Marginal revenue

I. Price-taker

J. Industry supply curve

5. The horizontal summation of the marginal cost curves of all firms operating in a market.

6. The change in total revenue when a firm sells an additional unit of output.

7. Costs which are independent of the volume of a firm's output in the short-run such as rent and rates.

8. A percentage increase in a firm's inputs leads to a bigger percentage increase in output produced.

9. The total costs of an enterprise expressed per unit of output produced

10. The best alternative use value of funds tied up in a business.

Exercise 2

Practical exercise

Strikes Ltd is a small firm specialising in the manufacture and retailing of carbon-fibre fishing rods. The rods currently retail at £60 each and are sold in a highly competitive market. The firm expects to be able to sell all it produces at this price but has no plans to raise the selling price in the short-run owing to the fierce competition it faces.

The firm has the resources to produce up to a maximum of 100 rods per week. An equation relating costs (£C) to output (X = number of rods) has been estimated by regression analysis to be:

$$C = 1{,}550 + 0.36X^2$$

(a) From the cost and revenue information provided, draw up a table to show the following over the range of weekly output 60-100 rods (in steps of 5 rods - i.e. 60, 65, 70, ... 95, 100):

   i) total, average and marginal revenue;

   ii) total cost, average total cost, average variable cost, and marginal cost;

   iii) profit.

(b) Determine the level of weekly output which is expected to minimise unit cost (i.e. cost per rod). What is the unit cost at this output level?

(c) At what level of output can the firm expect to maximise profit and what is the expected maximum level of profit?

(d) Use the revenue and cost information provided to determine an equation for weekly profits.

Exercise 3

Short-answer questions

1. Explain why the typical short-run average cost curve is U-shaped.

2. Why does the marginal cost curve pass through the bottom of the average cost curve?

Theory of the firm I

3. Explain the essential difference between an economist's and an accountant's concept of profit.

4. What is meant by the term 'external economies' and how do they influence a firm's long-run average cost curve?

5. What is meant by the term 'diseconomies of scale'?

6. Why can the marginal cost curve of a competitive firm, above the point at which MC = AVC (average variable cost), be regarded as its supply curve?

7. What are the main assumptions of the perfect competition model?

8. In what circumstances would the equality between MC and MR mean maximum losses for a competitive firm?

Exercise 4

Data response

Table 9.1 Income and Expenditure Account - Halifax Building Society (£m)

	1990	1989
Interest Receivable		
On secured advances	4,910.3	3,424.7
On other lending:		
- to associated bodies	8.2	0.4
- other	60.4	24.4
On fixed interest liquid assets:		
- interest	779.5	486.5
- net (losses)/profits	(25.1)	9.0
On other liquid assets:		
- interest	3.6	4.0
	5,736.9	3,949.0
Interest Payable		
Interest payable on retail funds, non retail funds, deposits and subordinate habilities		
- Interest	3,928.4	2.574.1
- Income tax on interest	867.8	630.6
	4,796.2	3,204.7
Other Income and Charges		
Commissions receivable	140.3	112.6
Commissions payable	(10.3)	(13.8)
Other financial charges payable	(1.2)	(1.4)
Other operating income	52.6	57.6
	181.4	155.0
Management expenses		
Staff cost	194.4	182.1
Depreciation	49.7	33.9
Other expenses	265.3	209.4
	509.4	425.4

Table 9.1. continued

	1990	1989
Provision for losses on loans and advances	48.7	8.8
	48.7	8.8
Tax on Profits on ordinary activities	209.4	170.2
	209.4	170.2

Source: Halifax Building Society. *Report and Accounts* 1990

Note: At the end of January, 1990 the Society's total assets were £47,986.8m of which cash, mortgages and other commercial assets were £47,589.7m.

(a) Select one item from the accounts which can be classified as a fixed cost and one which can be classified as a variable cost. Justify your answer.

(b) What were the Society's total revenue and total cost figures for the year ending Jan. 1990?

(c) What were the Society's gross profit and net profit for each of the two years shown?

(d) What is the percentage return on assets for the year ending Jan 1990?

(e) In what sense can measures of average cost and average revenue be obtained from the information provided? What approximate measures can be obtained for the year ending 1990?

Exercise 5

Essay questions

1. Explain, with the aid of diagrams, why firms operating in a perfectly competitive market may make either supernormal profit or losses in the short-run, depending on market circumstances, while in the long-run competitive firms will necessarily make normal profit.

2. A welfare argument for promoting competition in industry is that the practice of marginal cost pricing by competitive firms leads to an efficient allocation of resources:

   (a) Carefully explain the precise market conditions under which strict marginal cost pricing would be practised.

   (b) Briefly explain why marginal cost pricing leads to an efficient allocation of resources in the absence of market externalities.

3. (a) With the aid of examples, describe three different sources of internal technical economies of scale.

   (b) In the absence of any real scope for technical economies, firms may still be able to reduce unit costs by operating on a larger

scale. Explain how this might be possible by reference to three
different examples.

Exercise 6

Group discussion

FOOD FIRMS PUT THE SQUEEZE ON CUT PRICE CHAIN

Whitbread has told a new discount supermarket chain that it is charging
too little for its products. The brewing giant has informed Aldi, a
privately owned German retailer with two shops in the Midlands, that it
wants to see prices raised so its products are sold at near uniform
levels.

Sarah Lee, a leading manufacturer of frozen desserts, has also
expressed concern at the low prices being charged for its cheesecake.

Certain supermarket groups and their suppliers are under investigation
by the Office of Fair Trading after allegations of strong-arm tactics
against Aldi. The German company complained to the official consumer
watchdog that its British rivals, alarmed at the prospect of a food price
war, have put pressure on suppliers to refuse to deal with it. Last week
a notice in Aldi's Birmingham store apologised to shoppers for the
unavailability of two leading brands.

Manufacturers fear the cut price campaign being waged by Aldi could
damage their reputations and devalue household brand names. Under the
Retail Prices Act a manufacturer can with-hold supplies if goods are sold
at less than it costs to make them. The big supermarket chains have
denied putting pressure on food suppliers and react angrily to an
accusation of price fixing. The established supermarket groups are to
face a further assault from another cut price foreign rival, Netto, a
Danish owned chain, plans to open its first British shop in the Autumn.
Elsewhere in Europe food store chains expect to make 2% to 3% net profit,
in Britain they are making three times that amount Henrik Grundelach, the
company's general manager, said.

Source: *Sunday Times* 17th June, 1990

Theory of the firm I

The discussion takes the form of a private hearing of the issues under the chairmanship of the Director General of the Office of Fair Trading.

One group should take the role of the Aldi Supermarket chain to support their wish to trade freely with the products of their choice and at a price they consider appropriate.

Another group takes the role of the food manufacturers who claim that they should have control over who sells their products and at what price.

A third group will represent the views of the Consumer's Association.

ANSWERS

Exercise 1

Mix and match

A. 7	B. 9	C. 2	D. 10	E. 3
F. 8	G. 4	H. 6	I. 1	J. 5

Exercise 2

Practical exercise

(a)

X	TR	TC	ATC	AVC	MC	AR	MR	Profit
60	3,600	2,846	47.43	21.60		60	60	754
					45			
65	3,900	3,071	47.25	23.40		60	60	829
					48.60			
70	4,200	3,314	47.34	25.20		60	60	886
					52.20			
75	4,500	3,575	47.67	27.00		60	60	925
					55.80			
80	4,800	3,854	48.17	28.80		60	60	946
					59.40			
85	5,100	4,151	48.83	30.60		60	60	949
					63.00			
90	5,400	4,466	49.62	32.40		60	60	934
					66.60			
95	5,700	4,799	50.52	34.20		60	60	901
					70.20			
100	6,000	5,150	51.50	36.00		60	60	850

(b) Minimum unit cost at 65 rods. ATC = £47.25.

(c) At approximately 85 rods per week. Expected weekly profit = £949

(d) Revenue equation = $60X$

   Cost   equation = $1{,}550 + 0.36X^2$

   Profit equation (Revenue - Costs) = $60X - (1{,}550 + 0.36X^2)$

Exercise 4

Data response

(a) Management expenses are unlikely to change significantly in relation to volume of lening in the short run and therefore could be considered a fixed cost.

   Interest paid on deposits is a variable cost as it varies directly with the volume of deposits.

(b) Total revenue for year ending Jan. 1990 is £5,929.8 m

Total cost for year ending Jan. 1990 is £5,317.1 m (exlcuding provisions and tax.)

(c)

	1989 (£m)	1990 (£m)
gross profit	564.0	465.1
net profit	354.6	294.9

(d) Return on Assets is 1.17% for 1990.

(e) Only in the sense that costs and revenues are related to some measure of volume of business. The only possibility from the information provided is to relate these variables to total values of mortgages, cash and other commercial assets. It is then possible to measure the cost per £ of outstanding loans. This can be done for revenues.

£m Year ending	(1) total cost	(2) total revenue	(3) loans cash etc.	$(1) \div (3)$	$(2) \div (3)$
Jan 1990	5,317.1	5,929.8	47,589.7	0.111	0.124

Interpretation

The average cost of loans was approximately 11.1p per £ loaned for a year.

The average revenue from loans was approximately 12.4p per £ loaned for a year.

Exercise 5

Essay questions   1.

*   Carefully define a perfectly competitive market.

*   Note importance of the freedom of entry and exit assumption.

*   Carefully explain the terms normal and supernormal profit.

*   With the aid of diagrams, explain the market adjustment mechanism whereby a normal profit position is restored for both the cases where supernormal profit is temporarily made and where short-run losses are experienced.

*   Briefly consider what might have caused the short-run market disturbances leading to both supernormal profit and loss-making situations.

10 Theory of the firm II

In this chapter the focus of attention is on firms operating in conditions of *imperfect competition*. Under the traditional assumption of profit maximisation the pricing and output decisions of enterprises operating in *monopoly*, *monopolistic competition* and *oligopoly* markets are considered. Alternative motives for business behaviour are also considered which involve the maximisation of other variables - e.g. sales revenue - plus objectives which are concerned with satisfactory all-round performance rather than the maximisation of any single variable.

Monopoly

Although the legal definition of a monopoly firm is any enterprise having at least a 25 per cent market share, we are concerned in economics with those cases where a *single firm* dominates the market. A monopoly firm faces a downward sloping demand curve for its product which means a divergence between its AR and MR curves. Consequently profit-maximising behaviour involves charging a price in excess of MC and it can be shown that if a competitive industry was monopolised then, providing production costs remain similar, a welfare loss would result from the higher price and lower industry output associated with monopoly. Of course, monopoly firms might benefit from scale economies which reduce average costs, and the existence of certain state monopolies - e.g. electricity - points to the extreme importance of scale economies in some industries.

Differences in demand conditions within a market can make *price discrimination* profitable for a firm providing re-sale of the product can be prevented. For profits to be maximised, marginal revenue must be the same in each of the sub-markets.

The surplus profit made by monopoly firms can persist owing to the various *entry barriers* - e.g. patents and copyrights - which potential new market entrants face.

Monopolistic competition

Unlike perfect competition, the many small firms characterising this market type are involved in fierce non-price competition - e.g. advertising - in an attempt to establish brand loyalty and to improve market share. The similarity between rival firms' products means that each firm in the market faces a fairly elastic demand curve and that although the difference between AR and MR may be small, the profit-maximising price must be greater than MC. There is freedom of entry and exit for firms in this market which ensures that any surplus short-run profit will be eliminated in the long-run so that P = AC is the equilibrium position. However, firms will be producing levels of output which are below that associated with minimum possible AC.

Oligopoly

Competition between the few characterises oligopoly markets and the central point is that individual firms feel a need to take rival firms' likely reactions into account in making independent price and output decisions. This creates a possible *kinked demand* situation for individual firms and relative price stickiness is a consequence of this. The kink produces a break in the MR curve which means that firms may be able to continue maximising profits at the same price and output levels following changes in production costs.

Some form of *parallel pricing* - e.g. tacit collusion - can help to prevent possible price-war developments associated with independent pricing by firms and, if practised successfully, will remove the kink from the demand curve. While price competition might therefore be weak or non-existent, non-price competition in the form of advertising could be quite intense and represents one of the effective entry barriers faced by potential new entrants to the market.

Alternatives to profit maximisation

The divorce between ownership and control in large companies may mean that major decision-makers have no direct interest in profit beyond ensuring satisfactory dividends for shareholders and sufficient retained profits for necessary investment. So subject to profit constraints, management may go for *other business goals*, e.g. *sales revenue maximisation*, *growth*, etc.

Behavioural models of the firm, as popularised by Cyert and March, stress the need to examine how firms really do reach pricing and output decisions in practice. The claim here is that firms *satisfice* rather than maximise since they have multiple objectives and recognise potential conflicts of interest between various interest groups.

It has been argued that the practice of *cost-plus pricing* by firms based on average rather than marginal costs provides evidence that profit maximisation is not the typical business objective. However, variable mark-ups on costs, prompted by changing market conditions, may well be consistent with profit-maximising behaviour.

EXERCISES

Exercise 1

Mix and match

1. A dominant enterprise in a market with no serious rivals.

2. Obstacles to the entry of new firms into a market such as high setup costs, patents, etc.

A. Monopoly firm

B. Price discrimination

C. Surplus profit

D. Barriers to entry

E. Parallel pricing

F. Satisficing

G. Kinked demand

H. Oligopoly

I. Mark-up pricing

J. Technostructure

3. Firms selling similar products tending to vary prices together, either via some form of price collusion or by following an acknowledged market leader.

4. A concept which suggests that prices are likely to be relatively 'sticky' in oligopoly markets.

5. Firms aiming for satisfactory performance in relation to output, sales and profits.

6. A group of specialists, including managers, scientists and accountants, which effectively controls a large company.

7. Pricing by reference to either average variable or average total cost to include a margin for profit.

8. A market in which there are a few (at least two) rival firms with significant market shares.

9. The element of profit which a firm does not require for the purpose of keeping factors of production in their current location.

10. Firms with market power charging different prices for the same product or service to different groups of consumers.

Exercise 2

Practical exercise

Marvel Mixers Ltd sell their products in the UK market only. The company currently sells its food mixers at £50 each and can produce up to 500 per week with available resources. Variable costs per mixer remain at a similar level over this output range - approximately £30. The fixed costs attributable to the mixers have been estimated at approximately £5,000 per week consisting principally of rent, rates, depreciation and selling expenses.

The firm wishes to make as much profit as possible over the next few months, and management is rather concerned about the appropriateness of the current price levels. Consequently the relationship between demand for mixers (x) and selling price (P) has been carefully researched and the following estimated equation is thought to be currently relevant for weekly sales levels in excess of 250 mixers:

$$x = 1,200 - 15P$$

(a) Predict short-run weekly sales revenue and profits if the current price remains unchanged.

(b) Advise on the appropriate price level for the mixers showing clearly that this price can be expected to maximise the firm's weekly profit. What are the expected levels of weekly sales and profits?

(c) If the firm's objective was to maximise weekly sales revenue rather than profit, then how many mixers should it aim to produce and what price should it charge? How much profit can the firm expect to make per week?

(d) Suppose an increase in wages for production workers causes variable costs per mixer to rise to £32. How will this influence production plans, selling price and expected profit? Would the firm's price and output responses be any different if the objective was short-run sales revenue maximisation?

Exercise 3

Short-answer questions

1. What are the essential features of a monopoly market?

2. Explain why a profit-maximising monopoly firm will always set price above marginal cost.

3. In the case of a profit-maximising firm practising price discrimination, why must marginal revenue be the same in each of the sub-markets?

4. Explain why a short-run profit-maximising firm will not raise the prices of its products following an increase in fixed costs.

5. What are the main similarities and differences between monopolistic competition and perfect competition?

6. In relation to the kinked demand theory of oligopoly behaviour, what are the factors determining the extent of the break in the MR curve?

7. What are the main forms of non-price competition between firms in an oligopoly market?

8. Explain why firms aiming to maximise sales revenue cannot, in many cases, literally aim to reach the highest point on their respective total revenue curves.

Theory of the firm II

Exercise 4

Data response

Table 10.1

Humber Bridge Crossings (1984 – 1988)

Vehicle Classification	1984–1985	1985–1986	1986–1987	1987–1988	1988–1989*
Motor Cycles	55,483	56,068	51,469	48,982	48,396
Cars & Light Vans	2,568,543	2,787,793	3,016,305	3,373,918	3,592,994
Cars & Light Vans with trailers	34,724	35,144	35,475	37,253	37,506
Heavy Commercial					
– 2 axle	145,666	147,299	154,771	159,857	171,649
– 3 axle	39,016	37,305	34,774	35,700	35,746
– 4 axle	158,450	166,137	195,970	217,760	236,683
Light Commercial/ Mini Buses	54,456	63,365	115,569	128,870	139,801
Coaches	14,520	17,061	22,395	33,751	39,116
Exempt/Service Buses	101,038	88,823	97,401	93,030	95,848
Total	3,171,906	3,398,995	3,724,129	4,129,121	4,396,740

Note: From 1987–1988 Service Buses are included with Coaches.

Source: Humber Bridge Board

Table 10.2
Toll charges on the Humber Bridge

	1984	1985	1986	1987	1988
Cars & Light vans	1.00	1.00	1.20	1.20	1.50
Heavy Commercial Vehicles*	4.50–7.50	4.50–7.50	5.20–8.00	5.20–8.00	5.20–8.00
Light Commercial Vehicles	2.00	2.00	2.40	2.40	2.90
Coaches	4.50	4.50	5.20	5.20	5.20

* 2 axle-4 axle

Source: Humber Bridge Board (The factors affecting the pricing policy of the Humber Bridge Board are dissimilar to those affecting commercial organisations and cannot, due to problems of space, be fully discussed in the text.)

(a) What factors would determine the demand for bridge crossings?

(b) What opportunities exist for the Humber Bridge Board to operate a system of price discrimination on tolls?

(c) What relevance does the concept of 'operational gearing' have in determining the pricing policy of the Board?

(d) What economic case can be made for the bridge to be free of charge?

Exercise 5

Essay questions

1. 'Monopoly is always harmful to the public interest since it involves a lower market output and a higher market price than would be the case under competitive market conditions.' Discuss.

2. Carefully explain why some monopoly firms practise price discrimination while others do not. Illustrate your answer with reference to suitable examples.

3. Discuss the kinked demand theory of oligopoly pricing behaviour.

4. 'Since the major decision-takers in large companies are salaried managers, profit maximisation is an unlikely business objective for such enterprises.' Discuss.

Exercise 6
Group discussion

Business objectives survey (Humberside). How might we best determine the typical business objective(s) of private sector enterprises operating in Humberside using a survey approach?

Some points for consideration:

1. Questionnaire design - consideration of questionnaire referred to in data response exercise (Exercise 4).

2. Selection of a representative sample of firms - information source(s) for the purpose of obtaining a suitable sampling frame and sampling methods.

3. Best method(s) of contacting the firms included in the sample.

4. Problems of non-response and how these can be minimised.

5. A need for additional notes to supplement questionnaire information?

6. Information storage and retrieval - computer data files.

7. Methods of data analysis and inferences concerning the population. How might we use the sample results to test whether there is any significant association between business goal and legal identity of enterprise, or between business goal and type of enterprise?

ANSWERS

Exercise 1
Mix and match

A. 1   B. 10   C. 9   D. 2   E. 3
F. 5   G. 4   H. 8   I. 7   J. 6

Exercise 2
Practical exercise

(a) Weekly sales revenue = Px. $P = £50$

$x = 1,200 - 15P$ given

$\therefore$ $Px = (1,200 - 15[50]) \times 50 = £22,500$

Since $x = 450$, Total costs = $5,000 + 30(450) = £18,500$

$\therefore$ Profit = Revenue - Costs = £4,000

(b) Profit-maximising price = £55

Expected level of weekly sales = 375 mixers

Expected weekly profit = £4,375

(c) Number of mixers = 500 (full capacity weekly production with current resources)

Selling price = £46.67

Expected weekly profit = £3,333

(d) The firm will cut back production from 375 to 360 mixers per week. Selling price will be increased from £55 to £56 per mixer. Expected weekly profit will fall from £4,375 to £3,640.

If the objective was short-run sales revenue maximisation then, in the absence of a biting profit constraint, it would still wish to work at full capacity and would leave the selling price unchanged at £46.67. So, no price or output response and expected weekly profit falls from £3,333 to £2,333.

Exercise 4

Data response

(a) Population density, industry, price, alternative routes, employment pattern.

(b) Monopoly supplier, different elasticity of demand conditions for different user groups, user groups can be identified and separated eg by time, type of vehicle.

(c) Operational gearing is the proportion of the total costs which are fixed. In the case of a bridge this would be very high and the implications for pricing policy are:

* high levels of usage required to break even.

* little incremental cost of additional traffic.

* necessity for maximum usage often encourages price discrimination and off peak discounting

(d) Encourages industry into the area, increases labour mobility within the region, reduces the cost of living, improved communications.

Exercise 5

Essay questions

1. * Define a monopoly market and briefly contrast it with a competitive market.

* With the aid of diagrams, indicate that monopoly is only sometimes harmful to the public interest, in the sense described, since in some markets economies of scale yield considerable unit cost advantages for the larger firms.

* Mention the existence of state-run monopolies and the fact that UK governments have approved many mergers.

* Despite the lack of empirical evidence there remains the possibility that monopoly firms are technologically more efficient than competitive firms. Over time this would convert a lower market output and a higher market price into precisely the opposite for a monopoly enterprise.

11 Introducing the public sector

The *public sector* is that part of the economy which is directly
controlled by the state. It exists in all modern economies, although its
size will vary from country to country. The role of the public sector in
a market economy is to ensure that the market works well by promoting
competition and by providing a means by which contracts can be enforced.
There are, however, occasions when the market does not work well, and it
may not give the results society desires from it. At this point, the
state may step in and try to improve things, for example with regard to
the distribution of income and wealth, the functioning of the
macro-economy or the control of pollution.

**The size of the
public sector**

The ideal *size* of the public sector is an issue of considerable political
debate. Conceptually it is an issue which can be examined by two main
methods. The first is to look for the correct balance between the
provision of public sector and private sector goods. The second is to
compare the benefits of public spending with the *burden of taxation*; that
is to look for the point where Social marginal benefit = Social marginal
cost.

It is a common feature of all economies in the post-war years that
public sectors have grown in real terms, and in most cases as a
percentage of national income. In a period of recession this is a trend
that has proved particularly difficult to break because of the rising
costs of social security payments. A strategy which has proved sucessful
in the 1980's, has been that of controlling the level of expenditure
growth to below the rate of growth of the economy. This has meant that
real expenditure has still continued to rise, but public expenditure as a
percentage of national income has fallen. Also there has been a switch
in the emphasis away from income taxes towards indirect taxes, where the
public may be less aware of the burden of taxation.

**Explanation for public
expenditure growth**

In all societies, public expenditure depends in practice on the key
elements of need, capacity and will. All three are a question of
interpretation but as Wagner pointed out, as societies become better off,
there is greater pressure for public expenditure. This indicates that
society's *needs* grow with their capacity. The growth of the public
sector in the modern economy can be as a result of demand factors such as
the need to provide for a growing population, or a need to meet the
public's expectations as to the level and quality of services they
require. On the supply side, it is often the case that the cost of

Introducing the public sector

public sector services rises because of higher input costs, or because they are more labour intensive. Although increases in public expenditure may not appear to be too much of a problem in an era of rapid economic growth, in periods of economic stagnation they are. This is because without extra resources, increased state expenditure is at the expense of private spending.

EXERCISES

Exercise 1

Mix and match

A. Externalities

B. Market failure

C. Public sector borrowing requirement

D. Pareto efficiency

E. Property rights

1. Ownership of a resource with the right to use it, or to transfer all rights to it through sale.

2. The inability of the market to provide goods at the optimal level.

3. The point from which it is impossible to deviate to make one person better off without making another worse off.

4. Costs and benefits caused by the activities of an industry which are not reflected in a price.

5. The needs of the public sector for finance to support its spending in excess of its revenue.

Exercise 2

Short-answer questions

1. Why is it important to distinguish between state production and state provision of goods?

2. In what way has the PSBR in the United Kingdom been affected by the sale of public assets?

3. Has Wagner's law of ever rising public expenditures been borne out by the data relating to the United Kingdom?

4. How does the relative size of United Kingdom public expenditure compare with that of other advanced industrial countries?

Exercise 3

Data response

With reference to Table 11.1 on page 64, answer the following questions:

(a) Why is it necessary to exclude the privatisation proceeds from the figures of general government expenditure?

(b) Consider why it is helpful to have the four different measures of the trends in public spending.

(c) In what way did the increase in United Kingdom unemployment in the early 1980s affect the trends in spending?

(d) What are the possible explanations for the fall in spending of GDP in the late 1980s?

Table 11.1

	General Government expenditure (excluding) privatisation proceeds)		Money DDP[2]	General government expenditure (excluding privatisation proceeds)
	Cash £1 billion	Real terms[1],[2] £1 billion	£ billion	Per cent of GDP[2]
1973–74	32.0	150.6	74.9	42.75
1974–75	42.9	169.3	89.3	48
1975–76	53.8	169.0	111.0	48.50
1976–77	59.6	165.1	129.7	46
1977.78	64.4	156.8	151.1	42.75
1978–79	75.0	164.8	173.4	43.25
1979–80	90.3	170.1	208.1	43.50
1980–81	108.8	173.1	237.2	45.75
1981–82	121.0	175.4	260.4	46.50
1982–83	133.1	179.8	284.9	46.75
1983–84	141.6	182.8	309.2	45.75
1984–85	152.6	187.7	331.1	46
1985–86	160.8	187.7	361.9	44.50
1986–87	168.9	190.8	387.7	43.50
1987–88	177.7	190.5	429.5	41.25
1988–89	185.7	185.7	476.1	39
1989–90	200.5	187.4	517	38.75

[1] Cash figures adjusted to 1988-89 price levels by excluding the effect of general inflation as measured by the GDP deflator at market prices. The GDP deflator is assumed to increase by 7 per cent in 1989-90, and by 5, 3,5 and 3 per cent respectively in the years 1990-91 to 1992-93.
[2] To avoid discontinuities in the series, in this Table and elsewhere in the Autumn Statement, GDP at market prices and the GDP deflator do not take account of the effect on GDP of the change from rates to the community charge in England and Wales from April 1990 - see footnote 2 to

Source: Treasury, Autumn Statement, cmnd 879, November 1989, p.6, HMSO

Exercise 4

Essay questions

1. Can economic theory adequately explain the growth of the public sector in the twentieth century?

2. Analyse the practical problems of determining the optimum size of the public sector.

3. Why has the growth of the public sector become a source of concern?

4. 'Great nations are never impoverished by private, though they are sometimes by public prodigality and misconduct. The whole, or almost the whole public revenue, is in most countries employed in maintaining unproductive hands.' A. Smith, *Wealth of Nations*, 1976 edn.

   Would you regard the above statement as being correct today? Give reasons for your answer.

5. What are the implications for the public sector of a significant reduction in the level of defence expenditure?

Exercise 5

Group discussion

The following reasons are put forward for having a public sector:

(a) promoting competitors;

(b) providing goods not provided adequately by the private sector;

(c) dealing with externalities;

(d) enforcing contracts;

(e) redistributing income and wealth;

(f) promoting macro-economic objectives.

As a member of a discussion group, put forward the case for the state abandoning one of the above tasks and leaving it to the market mechanism to resolve the problem.

ANSWERS

Exercise 1

Mix and match   A. 4   B. 2   C. 5   D. 3   E. 1

Exercise 3

Data response

(a) Privatisation receipts are a source of income related to the sale of assets, and as such they do not reduce expenditure.

(b) Each measure tells us different things, for example the level of expenditure in real terms tells us what the trend of spending has been, once the impact of inflation has been removed. The level of expenditure in relation to GDP reflects the ability of the economy to actually sustain the level of spending.

(c) An increase in spending on unemployment benefit would raise the level of spending by the state, which may also cause public expenditure to rise as a percentage of GDP.

(d) The fall in spending as a percentage of GDP is clearly related to the fact that public expenditure was growing more slowly than the economy.

Exercise 4

Essay question   1. * There are a number of explanations as to why the public sectors of economies have grown. This question asks for a review of some of these.

   * The problem is finding a satisfactory explanation which fits for all time. Most theories really only work for one particular period.

   * Trying to explain current public expenditure growth in an era of stagnating growth is particularly difficult. The best suggestion is that it is related to public expectations as to improved services, and an open-ended commitment to pay welfare benefits.

12 Public goods and externalities

One way of trying to explain *public expenditure* decisions is to examine the way the market economy might fail to produce the optimum allocation of resources because of the existence of *public goods* and *externalities*. Public goods and private goods have a specific technical meaning in economics. Public goods are defined as those where the consumption of one person does not reduce the amount available to others (non-rivalry), and where it is not possible to exclude persons who have not paid towards producing them (non-excludability). In contrast, private goods are those where one person's consumption reduces their availability to others and it *is* possible to exclude others from consumption. The problem posed by public goods is that they may be highly desirable but, because of the existence of free riders, entrepreneurs may not provide them. Free riders are people who are prepared to take advantage of a service without contributing towards its cost.

In reality, there are few examples of pure public and private goods. Most goods fall under the category of *mixed goods*, that is they have features of both public and private good content. Mixed goods predominate within the economy and these produce spillover effects usually known as externalities. These externalities generate costs and benefits for others which are not taken account of by the market economy. This suggests that there is, in many cases, a difference between the socially optimum level of production and that generated by the market. Some externalities are said to be 'good', for example the benefit which society enjoys from a well-educated population. On the other hand, there are 'bad' externalities such as the effects of toxic waste disposed of by factories into the water supply. The existence of these good and bad externalities may cause the state to intervene. In the case of good externalities the state may stimulate their production, either providing subsidies or directly producing the goods itself. In the case of 'bad' externalities, the state will normally resort to regulation to try and control their output.

Cost-benefit analysis When public investment takes place with projects such as road building it is clear that a stream of benefits will result for motorists and perhaps to those people who find that there is less traffic nuisance. Although there is a return, the price mechanism is not in operation. *Cost-benefit analysis* can therefore be employed as a way of taking account of the *social* costs and benefits that emerge as a result of such a project. The measuring rod used is money, although practitioners have to *use shadow prices* in order to reflect the true costs and benefits from a project. For example, the savings from the avoidance of a road death is given a

Public goods and externalities

monetary value. Once the costs and benefits have been assessed, and discounted to obtain their present value, it should, at least in theory, be possible to compare similar projects and to make rational decisions as to investment priorities. Inevitably the methods used have been frequently criticised, not least because some items are impossible to value, and often projected benefits simply do not materialise.

EXERCISES

Exercise 1
Mix and match

1. A technique which attempts to evaluate the social benefits and social costs involved in public investment projects.

A. Shadow prices

B. Mixed goods

2. Individuals who see it in their self-interest to take advantage of a good without contributing towards its costs.

C. Negative externalities

3. The cost of activities borne by society as a whole that are not reflected in the individual firm's production costs.

D. Free riders

E. Non-rivalness

4. The warming of the earth's atmosphere and the associated changes in global weather patterns.

F. Cost-benefit analysis

5. Substitute prices, which attempt to reflect social costs and benefits of project.

G. Social cost

H. Greenhouse effect

6. Overflow effects which have a bad effect on society as a whole.

7. The availability of a good to extra users at zero cost.

8. The kind of good which has both a public and a private content.

Exercise 2
Practical exercise

The pollution of the river Hull. The data in Table 12.1 concerns the activities of a small chemical works on the bank of the river Hull. Traditionally, the firm has discharged the toxic waste into the river causing some hazards to the environment.

(a) Complete Table 12.1.

(b) Draw a graph and indicate the level of output that a profit-maximising firm would produce at.

(c) Indicate on the graph the socially desirable level of output.

(d) What level of tax would need to be imposed in order to reduce output to the socially desirable level?

(e) Discuss the problems faced by water authorities wishing to regulate the outflow of pollution into the river.

Public goods and externalities

Table 12.1

Units of output	Total private cost (£)	Total revenue (£)	Total social cost (£)	Marginal private cost (£)	Marginal revenue (£)	Marginal social cost (£)
1	200	500	250			
2	400	950	550			
3	600	1,350	900			
4	800	1,700	1,300			
5	1,000	2,000	1,750			
6	1,200	2,250	2,250			
7	1,400	2,450	2,800			
8	1,600	2,600	3,400			
9	1,800	2,700	4,050			

Exercise 3
Short-answer questions

(1) Why are there so few examples of pure public goods?

(2) In what way are the characteristics of mixed goods similar to those of a club?

(3) In what way might the payment of a subsidy help to generate a positive externality?

(4) How might the use of a tax discourage the production of negative externalities?

(5) Under what circumstances is it possible to get a conflict in the results for discounting the costs and benefits of a project by using net discounted present value, as against internal rate of return?

Exercise 4
Data response

A cost-benefit analysis of the Market Weighton by-pass. Market Weighton is a small town of 3,776 population which lies on the A1079 trunk road. Over the years the volume of traffic along the road has increased considerably in line with national trends. The problem for the town is that the main street is relatively narrow for carrying a high volume of traffic, and that the town is situated at the bottom of a long hill. In the past there have been incidents of runaway vehicles which have caused considerable damage. The vibration of the traffic is causing some damage to buildings; on the other hand, the town traders like the passing trade going through the town. There is no evidence that there are any appreciable delays to traffic through the town.

Public goods and externalities

Fig. 12.1 presents some of the possible routes that the by-pass might
take. There are something like 14,000 vehicles per day going through the
town, with about 25 per cent of these being goods vehicles.

Fig. 12.1

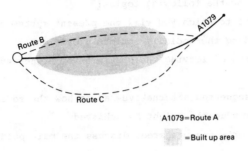

A1079=Route A

=Built up area

(a) In Fig. 12.1 you are offered three possible routes for the A1079 to
    proceed. Give your views on the suitability of each.
(b) How might cost-benefit analysis help to make a choice between routes?
(c) What are the implications of a cost-benefit analysis for the scheme's
    priority in the national road building programme?
(d) What are the shortcomings of any cost-benefit analysis being applied
    to such a scheme as this?

Exercise 5

Essay questions

1. Analyse the economic reason for the public sector either supervising
   or directly providing a household refuse collection service.

2. What are the economic arguments for and against an individual country
   opting to abandon its nuclear power programme?

3. Discuss the reasons why it is the state which normally deals with the
   effect of negative externalities.

4. Due to a period of very rapid commercial and housing development, the
   London dockland area is now facing severe problems of traffic
   congestion. The existing light railway is unable to cope with the
   growth in traffic, and so it has been suggested that the London
   underground system should be extended to relieve the pressure. How
   might cost-benefit analysis be useful in determining the desirability
   of building such an extension?

5. Analyse the reasons for the increasing role of national governments
   and the European Community in the management of environmental
   problems.

Exercise 6

Group discussion

It has frequently been suggested that because higher education students have a higher earnings potential, they should not be supported by government grants or other sources of public sector finance.

Break your class into three groups and prepare short reports for presentation on the following topics:

(a) the extent to which you view the present system of higher education as providing the socially optimum provision;

(b) the effects of leaving the provision of higher education to the market;

(c) provide suggested alternatives as to how the socially optimum level of higher education might be achieved.

Once the reports are prepared, discuss the main points in them and prepare a list of ten recommendations based on your findings.

ANSWERS

Exercise 1   A. 5   B. 8   C. 6   D. 2   E. 7   F. 1   G. 3   H. 4

Exercise 2

Practical exercise   (b) 7

(c) $3\frac{1}{2}$

(d) £175

Exercise 4

Data response

This is a problem-solving exercise and could well benefit from discussion in a group.

The problem with the alternative routes is that they both mean a longer journey for the motorist. In the case of route B, it would mean the road still going through a built-up area. This is an actual problem where a cost-benefit analysis was done which showed a by-pass might be worthwhile. However, it would appear that there are many schemes on a national basis which are equally or more worthwhile.

Exercise 5

Essay questions   1.

* This question involves a discussion of market failure and the problem of externalities.

* Refuse collection is a mixed good in that it involves both public and private provision.

* Although many people would organise their own refuse collection, there are always those who would be content to dispose of refuse in such a way as to impose significant costs on others in the form of disease or just nuisance.

13 Financing the public sector

The activities of the public sector are financed predominantly by taxation, although borrowing and printing money and the revenue from the state's trading enterprises also make a contribution. *Taxes* are important not only because they provide a source of revenue for the government, but also they help to influence the level of expenditure in the economy. They influence the pattern of expenditure and the distribution of income in the economy, and are generally a tool to achieve many aims of government policy.

Principles of taxation

Adam Smith suggested four principles of taxation. The first was that the tax system should be *equitable*. This can now be interpreted to mean that taxes should be placed upon individuals according to the benefits they receive from the state. Alternatively, citizens' ability to pay is regarded as the most important principle. This suggests equality of sacrifice might be important, but with citizens enjoying a wide variety of incomes and endowed with different levels of wealth it is difficult to find a satisfactory solution to the problem. Smith's second principle of taxation is that both the taxpayer and the state should be *certain as to the amount of tax they pay or receive*. The third is that *collection of taxes should be simple and convenient* and, finally, the *cost of collection should not be excessive*.

Direct and indirect taxes

Direct taxes are those which are levied on incomes and wealth, whereas *indirect taxes* are levied on goods and services. If taxes are imposed, they will have an effect on the behaviour of the public. In the case of indirect taxes, they can distort relative prices and so lead to a misallocation of resources. On the other hand, direct taxes may prove a disincentive to work. Although it is possible to illustrate this with economic analyses, it is also possible to show that the reverse might be true. Higher taxes may mean that individuals may be prepared to give up leisure in order to work longer hours and maintain their incomes.

Structure of taxation

In reality, any country's taxation system is made up of a mixture of direct and indirect taxes. Because they are more likely to be progressive, the UK has tended to favour direct taxes. This emphasis shifted in the 1980s when the UK opted for higher rates of indirect taxes in order to reduce some of the perceived disincentive effects of excessive direct taxes.

Financing the public sector

Finding a satisfactory method of funding local government has been a problem for a number of countries because their taxation system is often based on a system of property values. This means that the tax rate has to change on an annual basis to cope with the effects of inflation. There are also problems associated with having to revalue the taxation base itself as property values change. In addition, central government is often concerned that local governments might impose a level of taxation on citizens which is too high. The UK has introduced two new taxes to fund local government, the first is the *community charge* which is the standard charge paid by almost all adult citizens, the second is the *uniform business rate*.

Other sources of finance

A very obvious alternative to the state financing services is to charge the people who receive the benefit of services. This is not a practical alternative unless the beneficiaries are easily identifiable. An example would be education, where the direct recipients are known. However, this approach does not take account of the fact that many may not use the service if they have to pay for it. In this case the social optimum of the service may not be provided.

Governments' other major source of finance is borrowing. This is resorted to by most countries and is not a burden unless it is from overseas sources. If the money comes from its own citizens, interest payments are simply a redistribution from taxpayers to debt holders. Finally, printing money can finance state spending, although inflation may result if it is not kept under control.

EXERCISES

Exercise 1
Mix and match

A. Tax expenditure

B. Direct taxes

C. Tax havens

D. Tax base

E. Wealth tax

F. Tax burden

G. Progressive taxes

1. Any locality or nation that levies very low taxes on foreign residents.

2. Allowances which are used to reduce tax liabilities. Usually income tax.

3. The items which make up the objects to be taxed.

4. Where the proportion of income paid in taxes increases as income rises.

5. Taxes on income, spending power or wealth.

6. A poll tax used to finance local government.

7. A tax on the accumulation of assets.

H. Community charge

8. The weight of tax an individual or organisation pays.

Exercise 2

Practical exercise

Personal taxation. A single person who is earning £21,000 per year in 1990 is given a susbtantial pay award and finds that his salary has increased to £30,000 per year in 1991. He benefited from a single person's allowance of £2,995 but has no other tax advantages. In 1991 his personal allowance has been increased by 8 per cent and the tax bands were raised by 8 per cent. The tax bands are as follows for 1990.

Percentate rate of tax	Taxable income £
25	0- 22,300
40	over 22,300

Using the above figures:

(a) What amount of tax will he pay in 1990?

(b) What amount of tax will he pay in 1991?

(c) What are the changes in his marginal rate of taxation between the two years?

(d) What are the changes in his average rate of taxation between the two years?

(e) Assuming a 6 per cent rate of inflation, would the general public pay more or less income tax as a proportion of their income under the above circumstance, i.e. a 8 per cent increase in tax thresholds?

Exercise 3

Short-answer questions

1.   Under what conditions would an increase in the national debt be a problem for an economy?

2.   What is the likely outcome of excessive printing of money?

3.   Why is it important to have some indication of the incidence of taxation?

4.   What are the advantages of a value-added tax?

5.   Why are income-based taxes best used to achieve the objective of equality of sacrifice?

Exercise 4

Data response

The cost of tax relief in the UK

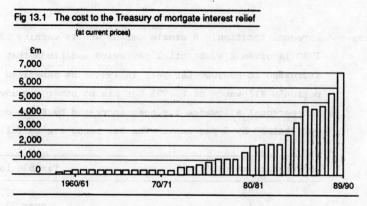

Fig 13.1   The cost to the Treasury of mortgate interest relief

(at current prices)

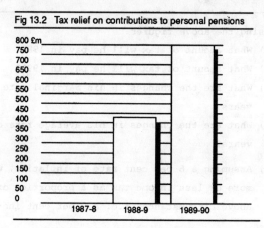

Fig 13.2   Tax relief on contributions to personal pensions

Source: *The Guardian*, 14th February 1990

(a) It has been suggested that middle classes are the main beneficiaries from the trends illustrated in Figs 13.1 and 13.2. Why is this likely to be the case?

(b) How do you account for the very steep rise in the cost of mortgage interest relief in the late 1980's.

(c) On what grounds can these tax subsidies be justified?

Exercise 5

Essay questions

1. Discuss the view that it is difficult to design a taxation system that is equitable.

2. Suggest ways that the taxation system may be used to promote social reform.

3. Consider the case for the introduction of a local income tax.

Financing the public sector

4. 'There is no such thing as a good tax' - Winston Churchill.
   Discuss the above quotation.

5. Discuss the view that higher taxation is a disincentive to work.

6. Why is it that almost all taxes on production fall ultimately on the
   consumer?

Exercise 6

Group discussion   Business in England and Wales has had a new system of paying its
contribution to local government imposed upon it. In the past, business
rates were set by individual local authorities, and they could vary
according to the part of the country that a business had its premises in.
In 1990 a uniform business rate was introduced which was based on the
revaluation of commercial property. As a result of the changes, areas
like the West Midlands have actually seen a fall in their rates bills,
whilst areas like Inner London are likely to experience a rise of 72 per
cent in their bills, with many retailing premises, such as Harrods facing
eventual increases of several hundred percent. (The changes will be
phased in over a five year period.)

Break into three groups and prepare to report to the commission set up
to investigate the likely consequences of these changes. Each group
should report on one of the following aspects:

(a) The problem of revaluation of property as a basis for taxation.

(b) The problem associated with moving towards a national system of
    property taxes.

(c) The benefits of local autonomy in the fixing of business taxes.

Each report should take account of the regional aspects of the problem in
their reports.

ANSWERS

Exercise 1

Mix and match   A. 2   B. 5   C. 1   D. 3   E. 6   F. 7   G. 4

Exercise 2

Practical exercise   (a) £4,501

(b) £7,631

(c) 25% to 40%

(d) 21.4% to 24.5% = 3.1%

(e) Less: the tax allowances have risen faster than the rate of
    inflation.

Financing the public sector

Exercise 4

Data response

(a) Middle class groups are the people most likely to take fullest advantage of mortgages to buy their house. However an increasing proportion of British society do own their own homes, so that the working classes also benefit from the system of relief.

(b) Rising interest rates mean that house buyers have to pay more to borrow the money to buy their homes. At the same time this means that they have a larger payment to claim relief against.

(c) Tax subsidies are a method of encouraging the public to do certain things. In these two cases, it is to buy their own homes, and take responsibility for their pensions. In both cases, it is hoped that there will be less reliance on the state section to provide for the citizen.

Exercise 5

Essay questions   1.
* The question asks for a discussion of the problems of defining what equity is, and the difficulty of applying the principle.
* Equity can be related to the benefits received from the system of public expenditure or ability to pay.
* Equality of sacrifice is particularly problematic.
* There are problems of deciding what can be taxed, for example should there be a wealth tax?
* Not all taxes imposed will have the effect that is expected of them if they alter behaviour.

14 Issues of public policy

The issue as to the degree of involvement of the state in the industrial economy has always been a contentious one. In all advanced economies, the state has not only increased its regulation of the private sector, it has also concerned itself with directly promoting change. In the past a considerable proportion of the UK economy used to lie in the hands of the state. This effect of asset sales has been to significantly reduce the size of the state owned sector. However, the state still has a major role in ensuring that activities of privatised utilities such as water, gas and telecommunications do not operate against the public interest.

Competition policy

If industry is left to itself, the degree of competition is likely to be reduced, and practices which are detrimental to the public interest are likely to emerge. In the UK, attempts to try and control *monopoly* and restrictive practices have tended to evolve and the results have been uncertain, especially in the area of monopoly. Greater success has, however been gained with regard to *restrictive practices*. Part of the problem with regard to monopoly arises from an uncertainty as to whether it is always a bad thing. In some cases, a dominant supplier is essential to gain economies of scale in order to compete in world markets. It has become increasingly clear that competition policy must also be viewed from a European perspective. The growth of the activities of companies across the single European market has meant that the European Community has assumed an important role in the regulation of comepetitive practices.

Industrial policy

Slow rates of growth and the wish to imporve the general level of economic performance has led most countries to intervene actively to improve their industry. Assistance given to declining industry to promote the restructuring process can be justified, as can aid being given to new areas of economic opportunity, but it can also distort the market mechanism. In particular it may well be that subsidies or special help given to one firm is at the expense of competitors. For this reason, assistance has to be carefully monitored, and on a European Community basis, state aids which gives an unfair advantage to a company are not allowed, and companies may even have to return illegal payments.

Nationalised industries

The problem that *nationalised industries* face is that their objectives are on occasion contradictory. They must obtain the bulk of their revenues from the sale of goods and services, and yet it is not clear if they should be serving the social interests of society or if they should be operating as would a private sector company. Some would argue tha both objectives are compatible in that state capitalists should operate as private capitalists and therefore achieve the best possible allocation of resources. In recent years, there has been an agreement that they should show a reasonable return on capital invested, but it is difficult to disentangle the industries from what has happened in the past when loss-making activities were forced upon them. Also, the protracted recession has had an effect on many industries, not just those in the public sector. Attempts to determine a reasonable method of pricing their products seem to have foundered. The suggested introduction of average incremental cost pricing made in the 1978 White Paper was for the sake of simplicity, but seems to have been an inadequate attempt to solve an insoluble problem.

Privatisation The term *privatisation* encompasses a number of measures which the UK Conservative government introduced after its election in 1979 to try and reduce the role of the state in the economy. These include the sale of state assets, promoting competition in areas like public transport, and the 'hiving off' of certain tasks like street cleaning to private contractors. A number of potential benefits have been identified, such as greater efficiency and independence of action. The greatest controversy has arisen with the sale of assets, largely because loss-making activities have proved difficult to sell, and the profitable ones have been underpriced in many cases. The potential of asset sales, to raise money for governments unwilling to raise taxes, has meant that there is now a world-wide interest in such sales.

EXERCISES

Exercise 1

Mix and match

1. The number and relative size of buyers and sellers in a market and the ease of 'access' to that market.

2. Short-term financial controls placed on nationalised industries restricting borrowing from outside sources.

A. Liberalisation

B. Hiving off

3. The strategy government adopts concerning the operation of an industry or industries in the economy.

C. Resale price maintenance

D. Nationalised industries

4. The commercial practices adopted in a market including anti-competitive practices.

E. Industrial policy

F. Market structure

5. Industries owned by the state which derive the bulk of their revenue through the sale of goods and services to the general public.

G. Market conduct

H. External financial limits

6. Removing barriers to competition in order to encourage free market conditions.

7. The practice of fixing prices for the retail sector by manufacturers.

8. The using of private sector contractors to do public sector tasks such as street cleaning.

Exercise 2

Short-answer questions

1. Distinguish between positive and negative policy.

2. Why is the small firms sector regarded as being particularly worthy of state support?

3. What are the benefits of economies of scale to our monopolist?

4. What was the impact of the banning of collective resale price maintenance for the retailing industry?

5. Distinguish between a monopoly and a restrictive practice.

6. Why have governments found a reason for keeping a golden share in privatised industry?

Exercise 3

Data response

Table 14.1   Privatised companies: trends in turnover, profits and employment[1]

Average compounded growth rates between dates

	Turnover (1987 prices)		Profits (1979 prices)		Employment	
	1979 to Privati- sation	Privati- sation to 1988	1979 to Privati- sation	Privati- sation to 1988	1979 to Privat- sation	Privati- sation to 1988
Commercial companies						
Amersham (1982)	3.6	12.6	0.0	16.1	–	6.4
Cable & Wireless (1981)	2.1	12.4	-11.5	24.1	–	13.7
Rolls Royce (1978)	1.7	10.8	–	0.0	-3.7	0.0
Jaguar (1984)	–	7.6	–	-4.7	–	6.6
Public corporations in competitive markets						
National Freight (1982)	-7.4	6.3	15.1	13.8	-11.1	2.6
Associated British Ports (1983)	-6.6	-0.4	-20.5	13.7	–	-7.8
British Airways (1987)	0.9	11.1	2.1	-1.2	-4.4	19.1
Britoil (1982)	39.8	-5.8	49.5	-22.8	–	-1.4
Enterprise Oil (1984)		-6.4		-27.1		39.3
Public corporations with national monopoly elements						
British Telecom (1984)	5.4	5.9	22.9	9.7	0.4	-0.3
British Gas (1986)	4.7	–	6.1	-9.4	-2.3	-2.2
BAA (1987)	0.9	11.1	20.9	39.6	0.7	1.4

1. Date of privatisation in brackets.
Source: OECE *Economic Survey of the UK*, 1988/9 p.92

Issues of public policy

(a) How does the performance of the three types of company compare in the periods prior to, and post privatisation?

(b) Consider the reasons for the variation in performance between the sectors.

(c) Using company reports and the media, examine the performance of these companies now. For example what has happened to Jaguar?

Exercise 4

Essay questions

1. Discuss the view that mergers are essential in order to gain the economies of scale required for competing in world markets.

2. Analyse the case for greater state support for private sector companies.

3. How can the public be protected from the harmful effects of the privatisation of a public sector monopoly such as the telephone system?

4. Analyse the problems of trying to achieve an adequate pricing policy for nationalised industries.

5. Does the fact that some nationalised industries make losses mean that they are not worth supporting?

6. Should a nationalised industry be compelled to meet social needs even when this conflicts with their overall profitability?

Exercise 5

Group discussion

TI Raleigh Industries are the largest producers of bicycles in the UK. In 1979, the company was responsible for producing 83 per cent of all bicycles made in the UK and had 46 per cent of the total UK market. Import penetration by foreign producers had risen from 34 per cent of the UK market in 1968 to 54 per cent in 1979. Raleigh enjoyed a reputation for quality cycles, and had considerable success in bicycle competitions. The company was investigated by the Monopolies and Mergers Commission because of the restrictive practices which it employed. In particular, there was a complaint that the company consistently refused to supply large discount stores such as Argos, although they did sell a third of their production to co-ops and mail order catalogue companies.

Raleigh argued that their restriction on trade was reasonable because:

(a) Large retailers were not committed to bicycle sales in the long run.

(b) Supplying large retailers would seriously undermine their 3,000-strong dealership network who were important in providing proper pre-sale preparation of machines and providing a good after-sales service.

Issues of public policy

The task of the group discussion will be to debate the merits of allowing Raleigh to continue with their restrictive practices from the point of view of:

(a)   the Raleigh dealers;

(b)   the large retailers;

(c)   the company;

(d)   the consumer.

ANSWERS

Exercise 1

Mix and match

A. 6   B. 3   C. 7   D. 5

E. 3   F. 1   G. 4   H. 2

Exercise 3

Data response   Whilst the answers to the questions depend on individual interpretations, it is clear that the trading situation of the companies and corporations involved do depend on the degree of competition that they face. In the case of the energy sectors we find that the oil corporations did badly in terms of declining profitability, as did British Gas. For those industries with a monopoly element, the extent of success depended on the degree to which the industry was regulated. Other factors to consider are the absence of total profit figures, and the degree of help given to the company at the time of privatisation. In the case of Jaguar, it was taken over by the Ford motor Company, in part because of poor company results.

Exercise 4

Essay question   1.   *   This question is about the desirability of mergers.

                         *   The case for them is that they allow firms to grow and become more efficient, not just from the point of view of production. It could well be that gains could be made in the areas of distribution and research and development.

                         *   Particularly in the manufacturing sector, competition is between world producers. Small companies may simply not have the resources

                         *   Mergers may, however, be used to reduce competition.

15 The determination of wages

In a market economy wages, like prices of most goods and services, are influenced by conditions of demand and supply. This has led one economist to suggest that the market for labour is little different from that of bananas. Both have prices which are subject to the laws of demand and supply; and (more controversially) a surplus of either can be eliminated by a fall in the equilibrium price.

Demand for labour

Demand for labour is a *derived* demand: labour is not employed for its own sake but for the goods and services it helps to make. Firms will therefore employ more labour as long as the extra cost is no greater than the additional revenue received by the rise in sales due to the extra products produced by that unit of labour.

Marginal productivity theory

Assuming the firm wants to maximise profits, it will hire units of labour until the last hired unit adds as much to revenue as to costs, i.e. Marginal revenue produce = Marginal factor cost.

With a perfectly competitive firm working in a perfectly competitive labour market, the cost would basically be the wage directly attributable to that last hired unit and the revenue would be the extra output produced times price of produce (value of the marginal product). The firm will then hire additional units of labour up to a point at which the wage is just equal to the value of the marginal product of labour.

However, where competition is not perfect, the position will be a little different. If the firm is a big employer of labour it may have to raise wage rates for all workers in order to attract an extra unit of labour. The marginal cost of employing the extra unit will therefore be *greater than* the wage. In addition, if the firm has some monopoly power in the product market it will only be able to sell the extra output produced by this extra unit of labour by *lowering* its product price. The extra revenue resulting from the sale of the output produced by the last hired unit of labour will be *less than* the value of the marginal product.

Supply of labour

The total labour supply at any one time is not fixed (i.e. not perfectly inelastic). Higher wages may increase the number of workers seeking jobs. Conversely, government legislation lowering retirement age or extending full-time education will lower the numbers.

The supply of labour to a particular occupation or geographical area will depend not only on the wage or salary levels but on other factors like qualifications, mobility of labour, trade union restrictions and the non-monetary advantages of the job.

The determination of wages

An individual might not always increase the number of hours he is willing to work, the higher the wage rate. As wage rates rise, leisure becomes more expensive relative to work and, after a certain level of affluence has been reached, an individual might wish to reduce his working hours if wage rates rise still further. The individual's supply curve of labour may therefore be backward bending.

Labour market imperfections

These include *produce monopolies, monopsonies* (one buyer of a particular type of labour) on the demand side and *trade union monopolies* on the supply side of labour.

Trade unions will attempt to raise wage rates through the power of collective bargaining. They will attempt to restrict the supply of labour via closed shops and the imposition of qualifications, and to force firms to pay higher minimum wages than would have been established in a freely competitive market. A link with government economic policy here should be noted. Some think high minimum wages should be imposed by the state for all workers and not leave it just to the lucky few who belong to strong trade unions. Others would disagree and claim high wages can cause unemployment by making capital cheaper relative to labour. This side might either want to reduce the power of the unions or to limit wage increases through a legally enforceable incomes policy.

EXERCISES

Exercise 1
Mix and match

1. Demand for a factor of production, not for its own sake, but for the goods and services it helps to make.

2. The change in total revenue resulting from the employment of one more or one less unit of the variable factor.

A. Closed shop

3. The change in total cost resulting from the employment of one more or one less unit of the variable factor.

B. Minimum wage

C. Marginal factor cost

4. The percentage of the potential workforce working or actively seeking a job.

D. Occupational mobility

5. Factors will move between different uses until there is no advantage, whether monetary or non-monetary, in another move.

E. Derived demand

F. Monopsony

6. Willingness of workers to move jobs.

G. Wage rigidity

7. Where all workers must belong to a trade union before they can be employed in a particular firm or industry.

The determination of wages

H. Substitution effect of labour supply

I. Hypothesis of equal net advantage

J. Marginal revenue product

K. Participation rate

8. As wages rise, leisure becomes more expensive relative to working and some workers opt to cut the number of hours on the job (is this one of the reasons for high absenteeism in Britain's coal mines today?).

9. One buyer only of a particular type of good, service or factor of production.

10. An agreement between employers and unions or a legally enforced dictate by the government which establishes the lowest wage paid to employees.

11. Where wages do not respond fully and quickly to changed conditions in demand and supply of labour.

Exercise 2

Practical exercise   Saturn Toys Ltd produce an electronic game which can be sold on the market at £15 per unit. The firm has a well-established brand name both in the UK and in the export market. The marketing department are confident that up to 15,000 units can be sold per week at £15. The level of output with the existing production capacity will vary in relation to the number of workers employed. It is assumed that no other factors of production are required. The labour market is perfect and workers can be attracted to the firm at the present wage of £100 per week in any quantity as required.

Number of workers (per week)	Total physical product (units per week)	Marginal physical product (units per worker/ week)	Price (£)	Value of marginal product (£)	Wage rate (£ per week)
0	0				
10	100				
20	300				
30	600				
40	800				
50	950				
60	1,070				
70	1,170				
80	1,240				
90	1,270				
100	1,270				
110	1,240				
120	1,180				

(a) Complete Table 15.1

(b) Draw a graph of the relationship between value of marginal product and the marginal cost of labour at different levels of work force size.

(c) Identify the numbers of workers which should be employed by the firm to maximise profits.

The determination of wages

(d) Draft a reply to the workers to explain the effect of a 30 per cent wage demand on the firm's employment policy.

(e) Recalculate the figures for a 10 per cent productivity gain due to a change in working practices and present a management offer to workers.

(f) Reply to an internal memo from the personnel manager discussing the impact of the formation of a trade union at Saturn Toys Ltd.

Exercise 3

Short-answer questions

1. Under what conditions is it likely to be easy for trade unions to gain significant wage increases?

2. What is the relationship between housing and labour mobility?

3. Outline the weaknesses of the marginal productivity theory of demand for labour.

4. A worker earns £3.50 per hour and works 45 hours per week. His wages then rise to £4 per hour and he is prepared to work only 42 hours per week. What is this phenomenon called, and why does it occur?

5. What is the economic justification for the very high earnings of a rock star like Bruce Springsteen?

6. Under what conditions is labour supply likely to be inelastic?

7. Why is it difficult to have a powerful trade union in the retailing trades?

8. Distinguish between official and unofficial strikes.

9. What action can a trade union take to shift the supply curve for a particular type of labour to the left.

Exercise 4

Data response

Salaries Well Above Inflation

Management salaries are rising at well above the rate of inflation, with further double figure rises like to be conceded by many companies, particularly in the South-east, according to a survey.

The result, says the Reward Group, which did the study, could be company failures and significant shedding of labour.

The survey involved 1,000 companies, employing more than a million people, and analysed the salaries of 26,123 working in senior management and in supervisory roles. Reward says that it is the most representative management pay survey yet published.

It found that last month, annual basic pay rises for managers averaged 11.8 per cent, compared with 11.1 per cent in September last year, 8.5 per cent in March last year and 6.4 per cent in September 1988.

Companies are now predicting that overall management pay will rise by

The determination of wages

9.1 per cent over the next year, but Reward says that experience suggest that this figure is more an expression of hope.

The survey found that employers, especially in the South-east and in the Thames Valley, expect to give rises of between 8 per cent and 10 per cent.

Reward warns that continued pressure on salaries could lead to problems for many companies. The survey says:

"Such a level of pay increases raises some very difficult questions. There is no doubt that employees are becoming intensely ware of their market value and that the lower levels of unemployment are producing lower levels of loyalty.

"The obvious and immediate solution for the majority of employers is to increase pay levels to beat off the competition.

Competition for staff would "raise salary levels and, in the low-loyalty, high-turnover areas, encourage employees to go on a merry-go-round. "Recruitment and training costs will spiral, along with salaries and payroll costs, Companies are already struggling to survive in an increasingly hostile financial environment and will have moved no further forward in stabilising their workforce."

Table 15.2 Average Management Pay

	Total Earnings	Increase
Chief Executive-General Manager	£20,946 to £47,838	10.5
Accounts-Financial Controller	£20,797 to £39,000	8.6
Company Secretary	£18,866 to £45,188	10.3
Construction-Contracts Manager	£15,418 to £25,030	19.9
Construction-assistant survery	£5,900 to £15,000	35.6
Computing Manager	£18,010 to £36,926	9.2
Engineering-Chief Engineer	£17,341 to £34,456	11.1
Marketing Manager	£20,732 to £36,680	9.3
Chief Personnel Manager	£18,536 to £35,913	6.3
Works Manager	£17,290 to £30,044	10.0
Chief Scientist-Technologist	£18,025 to £32,800	8.2
Sales Manager	£19,284 to £37,429	8.6
Legal Adviser	£23,655 to £49,160	16.5
Graduate Trainee	£8,209 to £13,000	11.2

Source: *The Times*, 19th April 1990

(a) What explanations can be advanced for the differences in management salaries shown in the table?

(b) How would you suggest companies could improve the 'low loyalty and high turnover' problems?

(c) Would you expect the figures shown in the table to be standard throughout the country?

(d) What are the problems in linking salaries to the level of inflation?

The determination of wages

Exercise 5

Essay questions

1. How far can the principles of free market economics be applied to the labour market?

2. Analyse the reasons why equal pay legislation has failed to equalise the earnings between men and women for comparable jobs.

3. 'If incomes policies are to be effective they must consider the distribution of income.' Discuss.

4. 'It is immobility of capital rather than immobility of labour which accounts for variations in regional employment.' Discuss.

Exercise 6

Group discussion

You are a group of workers employed within a new production plant. Your employees are anxious to create an atmosphere of industrial harmony.
They have asked you to present your attitude to the following proposals:
(a) free choice about union membership;
(b) a no-strike agreement;
(c) non-unionisation;
(d) a closed shop.
In order to come to consensus about these issues, break up into groups and present the case for each of these proposals using economic analysis where you can.

ANSWERS

Exercise 1

Mix and match

A. 7   B. 10   C. 3   D. 6   E. 1   F. 9

G. 11   H. 8   I. 5   J. 2   K. 4

Exercise 4

Data response

(a) Scarcity of skill and experience. Qualification level, variations in demand, earnings include bonuses and allowances.

(b) Better training and development of managers, job satisfaction, improved working conditions, better careeer opportunities.

(c) Wage drift likely to be considerable with higher remuneration in London area.

(d) Wage/price inflationary spiral.
Loss of competitiveness especially internationally.
Expectations created of automatic salary increases.
Comparability claims encouraged.

The determination of wages

Essay questions   1.

* Free market economists argue that the state should remove market imperfections from the labour market, e.g. trade union restrictive practices, wages councils etc.

* In addition, it is argued that reduced availability of welfare benefits would reduce the period of 'search' unemployment.

* These measures would then allow the free market to determine wages in accordance with demand and supply.

* Demand for labour is a derived demand and the principles of elasticity apply in relation to the elasticity of demand for the product.

* Supply of labour is generally determined by workforce size and distribution and more particularly to an occupation by occupational and geographic mobility.

* Some discussion is required on the social costs of a free market for labour, particularly with reference to depressed regions.

16 Rewards to factors of production

Distribution theory generally assumes a free market mechanism in which factors of production are employed to the point where the value of the marginal product is equal to the marginal cost of the last unit. In reality, factor markets are rarely free from imperfections. Factors of production are not homogeneous and do not transfer from one activity to another without time and expense.

The rewards to capital

Marginal productivity theory can be applied to capital as well as to labour. Rates of interest are determined by the interaction of supply and demand for loanable funds. The firm's demand for capital will vary inversely with interest rates as the *internal rate of return* on an investment project will tend towards zero at higher rates of interest. The supply of loanable funds will increase at higher rates of interest as households are attracted towards savings by the improved return.

Critics of this model point out that in reality capital is heterogeneous as existing buildings and machines have different life-spans. In addition, the assumption that households' savings are sensitive to interest changes is doubtful as much of today's savings is in the form of contractual payments, e.g. pensions, life assurance, endowment mortgages.

Theories of rent

Rent, as a reward to the suppliers of land, can also be analysed in the context of marginal productivity theory. Typically examination questions concentrate on the relatively high site rents for city centre locations. This is the case because the demand for any factor of production is a derived demand and therefore high rents can be charged because high prices for goods in city centres can be obtained from the strong demand conditions for the goods sold in the shops. Furthermore, supply of a particular type of premises will be limited in city centres due to their relative immobility between uses.

Much of the high level of site rent charged in city centres would be classed as *economic rent* which is a return in excess of opportunity cost. For example, if the site of a shop in a city centre could alternatively be used as a car park, that part of the rent paid on the shop premises which is in excess of the rent which could be obtained as a car park is economic rent. In reality, of course, the costs and time delays of transfer from shop premises to a car park in the event of the shop rent failing to reach transfer earnings cannot be ignored. In modern economics the concepts of economic rent and transfer earnings have come to be applied to all factors of production.

Rewards to factors of production

Exercise 1

Mix and match

A. Cobb-Douglas production function

B. Non-neutral technical progress

C. Economic rent

D. Transfer earnings

E. Internal rate of return

F. Quasi-rent

G. Average productivity of labour

H. Capital intensive

1. The payment required to keep a factor of production in its present use.

2. The output per unit of input employed.

3. The rate of discount at which the expected net cash flows are zero.

4. A function representing the relative share of labour and capital in the total product of a country.

5. The part of the payment made to a factor of production which is in excess of the amount required to keep it in its present use.

6. Where the ratio of capital to other factors of production in an industry is comparatively high.

7. Technical change which causes a shift in the proportion of labour and capital employed.

8. A short-term return to a factor of production in excess of opportunity cost due to temporary supply shortages.

Exercise 2

Practical exercise

A car manufacturer wishes to employ the least-cost combination of men and machines to produce 200 cars per week.

From past experience, it is known that all the combinations of men and machines given below would produce the required output of 200 cars per week.

Number of machines	Number of men
10	6,200
20	4,800
30	3,700
40	3,000
50	2,700
60	2,500
70	2,400

The cost of each machine to buy and run averages out at £5,000 per week. The wage rate is £100 per week.

(a) Calculate the least-cost combination of men and machines which could produce 200 cars per week.

Note This can be done graphically by plotting an isoquant (indifference curve) of combinations of men and machines which

would produce 200 units and finding the lowest possible
iso-cost line (budget line) at a tangent to the point of the
isoquant nearest the origin.

(b) What would be the least-cost combination if the cost of the machines
increased to £10,000 per week?

(c) What would be the least-cost combination if the wage rate increased
to £150 per week?

(d) What is the marginal rate of substitution of capital for labour if
the number of men employed reduced from 50 to 40?

(e) Explain the shape of the isoquant in terms of marginal rate of
substitution.

Exercise 3
Short-answer questions

1. What is meant by the sentence 'the marginal productivity of capital
will decline as the capital stock expands'? Why is this likely?

2. What do you understand by 'reswitching'?

3. Should energy be treated as a fifth factor of production?

4. In practice, what factors make capital a heterogeneous factor of
production?

5. Can transfer earnings and economic rent be compard with normal and
supernormal profits?

6. 'The prices of cinema seats in Central London are high because rents
are high.' What truth is there in this statement?

7. Rent is a scarcity payment, do you agree?

Exercise 4
Data response

With reference to Table 16.1 answer the following questions.

(a) Why is it better to make inter-firm comparisons on profitability by
using the profit as a percentage of capital employed?

(b) Why has profit before tax in (Commercial Services and the food and
drink distributors) industry increased and yet the percentage profit
in relation to capital employed has fallen?

(c) What factors account for the trends in profitability over the period
shown in the data?

(d) To what extent can profit be regarded as a measure of economic
efficiency in an industry?

Rewards to factors of production

Table 16.1 Profits in select UK industries

	Profit before tax (£m.)			Profit/Capital Empld percentage		
	1987/88	1986/87	1985/86	1987/88	1986/87	1985/86
Commercial Services	798	786	656	29.1	34.0	32.0
Industrial Services	318	237	170	25.1	22.5	18.7
Timber & Furniture Industry	421	272	166	24.0	19.3	14.1
Building Materials Industry	753	543	373	23.3	19.4	15.1
Transport Industry - Distributors	577	429	345	22.6	17.6	16.6
Chemical & Plastics Industry	4,430	3,632	3,038	22.4	19.3	17.9
Electronics Industry	6,493	5,820	5,046	21.7	20.8	19.1
Food & Drink Distributors	1,860	1,576	1,241	20.8	23.1	21.7
Retailing Industry	4,422	3,901	3,240	20.3	21.3	20.3
Paper, Printing & Packaging Industry	859	674	482	19.9	18.0	15.1
Textiles & Footwear Manufacturers	720	639	524	19.0	18.2	16.7
Food Manaufacturers	2,789	2,310	1,942	17.9	17.3	16.1
Consumer Goods Manufacturers	237	212	141	17.8	19.2	14.0
Publishing Industry	329	244	147	17.7	16.0	12.4
Oil, Gas & Mining	3,034	2,887	5,468	17.6	20.0	43.4
Electrical Industry	344	247	285	16.8	12.6	15.7
Ceramics & Glass Industry	446	345	215	16.6	13.5	10.3
Metals Industry	178	119	109	14.4	10.4	9.4
Engineering Component Manufacturers	264	217	201	14.4	12.2	12.0
Drinks Industry	1,483	1,217	1,040	12.5	11.4	11.2
Engineering Equipment Manufacturers	172	153	118	11.2	10.2	7.9
Industrial Equipment Manufacturers	972	1,363	1,151	10.7	15.6	14.4
Consumer Services	727	585	471	10.3	12.5	13.4
Construction Industry	3,250	2,113	1,539	10.3	9.0	8.0
Transport Industry - Services	369	282	305	9.4	8.1	9.6
Engineering Services Industry	51	45	68	8.7	8.1	12.6
Transport Industry - Manufacturers	348	432	451	5.2	7.4	8.1

Source: *Industrial Performance Analysis*, 1989/90

Exercise 5

Essay questions　　　1.　'Wages in an industry should rise in line with productivity only.'
What are the implications of this statement?

Rewards to factors of production

2. Can minimum wage legislation have a role to play in alleviating poverty?

3. To what extent can the oil revenues to OPEC countries be regarded as economic rent?

4. Should profit-sharing schemes be more widely adopted in British industry?

5. 'Normal profits are the supply price of entrepreneurship to a particular industry.' Discuss.

Exercise 6

Group discussion

You are the project team for a property development company based in Oxford. A site has come to your attention approximately one mile from the city centre. Outline planning consent has been granted for the erection of nine terraced houses in two blocks with nine garages in a detached block. Two semi-detached cottages on the site require demolition. As an alternative development proposal you have been asked to consider a block of fourteen flats with garages in a separate block. Sealed bids for the purchase of the site must be sent to the estate agent handling the sale.

Cost estimates have been made for the alternative developments as follows:

	£
Demolition and site clearance	7,500
Construction cost of houses (per house)	25,000
Construction cost of 9-garage block	12,000
Construction cost of 14 flats	295,000
Construction cost of 14-garage block	15,000
Legal costs for houses	10,000
Legal costs for flats	12,500
Other costs (for either development)	25,000

The sales department estimate that in the present market conditions in Oxford the houses could be sold for £45,000 each (freehold) and that 99-year leases for the flats could be sold for £35,000 each.

Company policy generally requires a 15 per cent return on houses and a 17.5 per cent return on flats but has accepted a lower return if this can be justified on the grounds of competitive tendering.

The class should be split into groups of 3-5 people at the beginning of the exercise.

Each group should consider what price they are willing to pay for the site on the basis of the information provided.

At an agreed time, each group should submit their sealed bid to the tutor.

A discussion should then follow on:

1. The reasoning behind each of the bids.
2. The successful bid.
3. Why the firm may be willing to reduce profit margins to secure a successful tender.
4. Why the return on flats should be higher than houses?
5. What is the difference between freehold and leasehold?
6. What objections might be made to the planning permission for flats?

ANSWERS

Exercise 1

Mix and match

A. 4	B. 7	C. 5	D. 1
E. 3	F. 8	G. 2	H. 6

Exercise 4

Data response

(a) Profit as a percentage of capital employed allows comparisons of companies of different sizes. It gives a more realistic assessment of the return in relation to the resources used.

(b) An increase in capital employed.

(c) Most industries in Table 16.1 show a significant increase in profitabililty over the period shown. This could be due to:

    i) Rising consumer demand due to increasing real wages and credit availability;

    ii) Greater productivity in the UK industries due to labour 'shake-out';

    iii) Greater efficiency in resource use with new technology;

    iv) Improved export competitiveness.

(d) Profit not a good measure of efficiency:

    i) High profits can result from monopoly control of supply or restrictive practices.

    ii) Profits can be made from 'windfall' changes in exogenous variables, e.g. high bank profits due to high interest rates.

    iii) Profits can be made from speculation on the foreign currency or markets or in property speculation.

Profit a good measure of efficiency:

    i) Major improvements in nationalised industry profits are due to

Rewards to factors of production

> reduced overmanning and higher productivity, e.g. British Steel.
>
> ii) In a competitive industry, a profit is a reward for innovation.
>
> iii) Profit can be a reflection of relatively low unit cost and technical efficiency.
>
> iv) Profit yields direct funds to finance new investment and technological efficiency.

Exercise 5

Essay questions

1.

* Productivity gains are made by the existing resources being used more efficiently to produce a higher output or by maintaining existing output with reduced resources.

* In the latter case, the implications are that wages can only be increased at the expense of employment.

* The former case implies that additional output can be sold in the market without reductions in revenue. Consider the possibility that the increased output may depress the market price.

* The statement assumes profit and productivity will increase in direct proportion.

* The statement assumes productivity gains from harder work by employees. In fact, gains can equally be made by more efficient management.

* Consider the difference between money and real wages.

* Should wages rise in line with profits?

17 Introducing macroeconomics

Macroeconomics is concerned with the identification, measurement and analysis of economic aggregates. The behaviour of such aggregates can determine crucial changes in employment, inflation, foreign trade and the standard of living, with profound consequences on all aspects of life within a country. An understanding of why changes occur and how the adverse effects can be prevented or modified is at the very centre of contemporary debate. Trends in the behaviour of these aggregates over several years are used in the evaluation of economic progress and policy measures, form the basis of economic forecasting and are used for international comparisons of economic performance.

Techniques of
measurement

The three approaches to measurement of national income are by *income*, by *expenditure* and by *output*. These components are usually referred to as identities as they are by definition equal. With adjustments for accounting refinements, e.g. taxes and subsidies, the final value of goods and services produced in the economy in one year must equal the factor incomes generated in producing those goods and services. In the same way expenditures made to buy those goods and services must equal the final value of the national output since the price of goods and services is determined by the factor costs involved in making them.

 The simplest and most accurate of the three approaches is the *expenditure approach*. The sum of consumption expenditure ($\underline{C}$), investment expenditure including changes in stock ($\underline{I}$), final government expenditure ($\underline{G}$) and the net foreign trade expenditure ($\underline{X}$ - $\underline{M}$) gives *Gross Domestic Product at market prices*. Care should be taken to include only final expenditures to avoid double counting. From here, three accounting adjustments are required to refine the final total.

(a) The *factor cost adjustment* (GDP market prices to GDP factor cost). This adjustment removes expenditure taxes and adds back subsidies.

(b) The *net property income adjustment* (GDP factor cost to GNP factor cost). This adjustment removes income generated within the economy which is paid to overseas owners of productive resources and adds back income generated abroad which is paid to domestic owners of foreign productive resources.

(c) The *capital consumption adjustment* (GNP factor cost to NNP factor cost). This adjustment deducts the depreciation on capital goods.

 GDP at *factor cost* can also be calculated by taking the sum of the value of the final outputs of all the domestic industries. Adjustments are required for stock appreciation and for the imported components of the final output. The last possible approach to the calculation of national income is a total of all factor incomes excluding transfer payments.

Problems of
interpretation

Most examination questions tend to concentrate on the difficulties of interpretation of national income accounts.

(a) *Current and constant prices*. It is important to realise that an increase in money GNP figures over several years is meaningless without corresponding information on price changes as the value of the national output may rise without an actual increase in physical output. Thus figures at current prices should be used with extreme caution.

(b) *Income distribution*. Increases in national income may well imply that the country is better off but in reality this may mean that it applies only to particular sections, e.g. a ruling elite.

(c) *The black economy*. Not all economic activity is conducted in money form or is adequately recorded. In comparisons between industrial nations and less developed countries, the latter's GDP may be understated due to a higher incidence of self-sufficiency.

(d) *Population changes*. Changes in the size and structure of the population need to be considered before judgements on the standard of living can be made from national income figures.

(e) *Negative externalities*. Economic growth resulting in GNP growth may have adverse effects on the environment, e.g. pollution which will reduce the overall welfare gain to the society.

(f) *Exchange rates*. International comparisons of national income have to be done in a common currency (usually the dollar). Any changes in the dollar exchange rate will therefore distort the figures.

(g) *Working conditions*. GNP growth may be achieved at the cost of worsening conditions of employment and so adversely affecting qualitative measures of living standards, e.g. longer hours of work, reduced holidays, higher personal risks.

EXERCISES

Exercise 1

Mix and match

1. The total final sale value of all goods and services produced by resources located in the UK excluding expenditure taxes and including subsidies in one year.

A. GDP at factor cost

B. GNP at factor cost

2. The total expenditure by households on goods and services which yield utility in the current period.

C. Real NNP at factor cost

3. The value at factor cost of interest, dividends and profits generated by British-owned resources located abroad minus the interest dividends and profits generated by foreign-owned resources located in the UK.

D. Consumption

E. Savings

F. Investment

G. Negative externalities

H. Net property income from abroad

4. The final sale value of all goods and services produced by resources located in the UK in one year excluding expenditure taxes, including subsidies and including net interest, dividends and profits from abroad.

5. That part of disposable income which is not spent in the current period.

6. Goods and services produced not for current consumption which facilitate a flow of benefits in future periods.

7. The costs imposed on society which result from an increased level of economic growth.

8. The final sale value of all goods and services produced by resources located in the UK in one year adjusted for inflation, capital consumption, excluding expenditure taxes and including subsidies and including net interest, dividends and profits from abroad.

Exercise 2

Practical exercise

A country has records of changes in economic activity over the last 10 years as shown in Table 17.1.

Table 17.1

	Figures in £m. at current prices	
	1980	1990
Consumer expenditure	27,000	32,000
Public authority final expenditure	8,000	11,000
Gross domestic fixed capital formation	8,000	6,000
Physical changes in stock	1,000	2,000
Imported goods and services	10,000	13,000
Pensions and family allowances	3,000	4,000
Rents	2,000	2,000
Exported goods and services	8,000	7,000
Taxes on expenditure	3,000	4,000
Subsidies	1,000	2,000
Gross wages and salaries	35,000	38,000
Gross income from self-employment	2,000	2,000
Property payments made abroad	3,000	4,000
Property incomes from abroad	6,000	3,000
Dividends	1,000	1,000
Capital consumption	2,000	3,000
Unemployment benefit	4,000	4,000
Population size	10m.	12m.
GDP price index (1970 = 100)	160	200

(a) Calculate the real GDP at factor cost for both years.

(b) Calculate the average standard of living for both years.

(c) Calculate the real NNP for both years.

(d) Comment on the economic progress of this country over the last 10 years with particular reference to any economic problems they might be facing currently.

Exercise 3
Short-answer
questions

1. What is the difference between a person doing their own painting and decorating at home and the same person doing painting and decorating for a living as far as the national income accounts are concerned?

2. Why are transfer payments always excluded from national income statistics? Give examples of transfer payments.

3. How is it possible for real GDP figures to rise over several years with substantial increases in unemployment at the same time?

4. Why is it necessary to distinguish between planned aggregate demand and supply and actual national expenditure and output?

5. If a large number of housewives gained employment in firms producing labour-saving domestic appliances and used their earnings to buy additional labour-saving devices to do the housework, how would this affect GDP? Is this an artificial effect?

6. How does the time students sit in lectures contribute to GNP?

Exercise 4
Data response

With reference to Table 17.2 on following page, answer the following questions.

(a) What conclusions can be drawn about the relative standards of living in each country?

(b) What are the dangers in making international comparisons on such data?

(c) Comment on the potential market in each country for UK exporters from the point of view of:

  (i) an industrial machine tool manufacturer;

  (ii) a household electrical goods manufacturer;

  (iii) a financial services consultancy.

Exercise 5
Essay questions

1. A large proportion of the employment in industrially advanced countries would be either unnecesssary or provided free of charge in less developed countries and therefore the per capita real growth in Western economies is far less impressive than conventional figures suggest. Explain and discuss.

2. Discuss whether or not changes in national income give an accurate assessment of economic welfare (a) over time, (b) between countries.

3. The 'black economy' has been estimated at anywhere between 2 and 10 per cent of GNP in the UK. What do you understand by this term and

Table 17.2   Revised figures

	Units	Reference period[1]	Australia	Austria	Belgium	Canada	Greece	Iceland	Ireland	Italy
Population										
Total	Thousands	1987	16 249	7 575	9 868	25 803	9 998	245	3 542	57 331
Inhabitants per sq. km	Number	1987	2	90	324	3	76	2	50	190
Net average annual increase over previous 10 years	%	1987	1.4	0.0	0.0	1.0	0.7	1.0	0.8	0.3
Employment										
Total civilian employment (TCE)	Thousands	1987	7 079	32 997	3 645 (86)	11 954	3 601 (86)	117 (86)	1 068 (86)	20 584
of which: Agriculture	% of TCE		5.8	8.6	2.9	4.9	28.5	10.3	15.7	10.5
Industry	% of TCE		26.6	37.7	29.7	25.3	28.1	36.8	28.1	32.6
Services	% of TCE		67.6	53.7	67.4	69.8	43.4	53.0	55.5	56.8
Gross domestic product (GDP)										
At current prices and current rates	Billion US$	1987	193.7	117.2	138.9	410.9	47.2	5.3	29.4	758.1
Per capita	US$		11 919	15 470	14 071	16 019	4 719	21 813	8 297	13 224
At current prices using current PPP's	Billion US$	1987	204.9	88.4	116.5	444.5	63.6	3.8	26.7	702.5
Per capita	US$		12 612	11 664	11 802	17 211	6 363	15 508	7 541	12 254
Average annual volume growth over previous 5 years	%	1987	3.7	1.8	1.5	4.2	1.4	3.1	1.8	2.6
Gross fixed capital formation (GFCF)	% of GDP	1987	23.8	22.6	16.3	21.0	17.4	18.8	17.4	19.9
of which: Machinery and equipment	% of GDP		11.5 (86)	9.7	7.0 (86)	6.9 (86)	7.1	6.5	9.4 (86)	10.0
Residential construction	% of GDP		4.7 (86)	4.6 (86)	3.4	6.4 (86)	4.6	3.5	4.6 (86)	5.2
Average annual volume growth over previous 5 years	%	1987	1.7	2.3	2.0	4.8	-2.2	1.8	-3.7	2.8
Gross saving ratio	% of GDP	1987	20.3	24.1	17.6	18.8	14.7	15.2	18.6	20.9
General government										
Current expenditure on goods and services	% of GDP	1987	18.2	19.0	16.3	19.5	19.5	17.7	18.0	16.7
Current disbursements	% of GDP	1987	35.0 (86)	46.6 (86)	51.6 (86)	43.3 (86)	42.9 (86)	27.3 (86)	49.2 (84)	45.2
Current receipts	% of GDP	1987	34.7 (86)	47.9 (86)	45.0 (86)	39.4 (86)	36.6 (86)	32.1 (86)	43.3 (84)	39.3 (86)
Net official development assistance	% of GNP	1987	0.33	0.17	0.49	0.47		0.05	0.20	0.35
Indicators of living standards										
Private consumption per capita using current PPP's	US$	1987	7 389	6 535	7 593	10 059	4 273	9 930 *	4 378	7 543
Passenger cars, per 1 000 inhabitants	Number	1985		306 (81)	335 (84)	421 (82)	127	431	206 (83)	355 (84)
Telephones, per 1 000 inhabitants	Number	1985	540 (83)	460 (83)	414 (83)	664 (83)	373	525 (83)	235 (83)	448 (84)
Television sets, per 1 000 inhabitants	Number	1985		300 (81)	303 (84)	471 (80)	158 (80)	303	181 (80)	244 (84)
Doctors, per 1 000 inhabitants	Number	1985		1.7 (82)	2.8 (84)	1.8 (82)	2.8 (83)	2.4 (84)	1.3 (82)	3.6 (82)
Infant mortality per 1 000 live births	Number	1985	9.2 (84)	11.0	9.4	9.1 (83)	14.1	5.7	8.9	10.9
Wages and prices (average annual increase over previous 5 years)										
Wages (earning or rates according to availability)	%	1987	5.7	4.9	3.4	3.6	17.4		8.8	10.5
Consumer prices	%	1987	7.0	3.0	3.5	4.2	19.3	25.7	5.2	7.6
Foreign trade										
Exports of goods, fob*	Million US$	1987	26 484	27 084	82 824[7]	94 320	6 516	1 368	15 948	116 004
as % of GDP	%		13.6	23.0	59.8	22.8	13.9	25.8	54.8	15.4
average annual increase over previous 5 years	%		4.4	11.6	9.6	6.5	8.7	13.7	14.6	9.6
Import of goods, cif*	Million US$	1987	26 964	32 580	82 992[7]	87 528	13 116	1 584	13 620	124 596
as % of GDP	%		13.9	27.7	59.9	21.1	27.9	29.9	46.8	16.6
average annual increase over previous 5 years	%		2.8	10.8	9.4	9.7	5.6	10.8	5.9	7.7
Total official reserves	Million SDR's	1987	6 441	6 049	7 958[7]	5 778	2 007	221	3 393	23 631
As ratio of average monthly imports of goods	Ratio		3.4	2.6	1.4	0.9	2.2	2.0	3.5	2.7

Source: OECD Report 1990

how far could a growth of the black economy indicate an improvement in the economic performance of the UK?

4. 'As every economist knows calculations of GNP are largely an exercise in statistical imagination, and even if they were accurate the GNP itself can be a very poor measure of welfare.' Discuss.

5. According to the IMF statistics in 1988 South Africa had a per capita GDP of $2630 whil Zambia had a per capita GDP of $370. What are the dangers in making comparisons on the relative standards of living in these two countries on the basis of these figures?

Exercise 6

Group discussion

The discussion should take the form of a public enquiry which has been commissioned to consider views on the proposals to set up ten nuclear waste reprocessing plants at different locations in the UK before 1995. Members of the group should represent views of the following organisations: the government; industrialists; the trade unions; environmental groups; local residents at the proposed sites.

The discussion should try to consider the balance of arguments between the quantitative aspects of economic growth, e.g. employment, GNP, foreign earnings and investment, against the qualitative aspects of the standard of living, e.g. the environment, personal safety. Further points for discussion might include:

(a) whether the reprocessing plants should be privately or publicly owned;

(b) whether it is better to concentrate the plants all at one site;

(c) by what other ways can pressure groups influence political decisions?

ANSWERS

Exercise 1

Mix and match

A. 1   B. 4   C. 8   D. 2
E. 5   F. 6   G. 7   H. 3

Exercise 2

Practical exercise

(a) £25,000m (1980), £21,500m (1990).

(b) £2,500 (1980), £1,792 (1990), calculated from factor cost GDP.

(c) £25,625m (1980), £19,500m (1990).

(d) Growth in population and inflation have reduced real per capita national income:

* fall in property incomes by 1986;

* serious balance of payments deficit by 1986;

* drop in GDFCF has implications for future economic growth.

Exercise 4

Data response

(a) SOL measured by factor cost GDP per capita.

Canada, Belgium and Austria have relatively high SOL.

SOL can also be indicated by infant mortality, balance of employment between sectors, passenger cars and TV sets.

(b) Dangers of international comparisons are: international differences in record keeping, self-sufficiency, unrecorded incomes and non-money factors e.g. hours of work, pollution.

(c) (i) High level of GDFCF important for a machine tool manufacturer.

(ii) Potential market for electricals indicated by GDP growth, TV sets.

Proportion of GDP expected to be imported would be important to UK exporters.

(iii) Financial services consultant would have a good potential market in countries with well developed tertiary sector.

Exercise 5

Essay questions

1. This question is based on the views of Misham and others that complex Western societies have created a vast number of unnecessary jobs which generate income which would not be counted in national income calculations.

* Many tertiary services in health and welfare are needed only because of the pressure of modern industrial societies, e.g. social workers, youth workers.

* Expenditure and employment on pollution control only results from uncontrolled economic growth.

* Tertiary employment in transport and the environment created by commuter traffic due to urban sprawl.

* Employment in education, the media and information technology also created by industrial society.

* Much of the welfare and social work in LDCs would be provided by the community without charge.

18 National income and employment

This chapter lays the foundations to understanding contemporary economic debate on employment by considering the process by which national income changes and the way in which equilibrium is attained. Much of the debate concerns the extent to which unemployment can be considered 'voluntary' or 'involuntary'. *Voluntary unemployment* is said to result from imperfections in the labour market which can be surmounted by the individual worker and is therefore avoidable by flexibility and personal initiative. By contrast, those who view unemployment as *involuntary* would attribute the blame to deficiencies in aggregate demand which go well beyond the power of the individual worker to control.

The classical view

The classical view is that full employment is attainable if the labour markets are allowed to operate without restriction. Unemployment results from the surplus labour which occurs when the supply of labour exceeds demand and can be corrected by the market clearing mechanism of reductions in wages. Thus the labour market is identical to any other market. The free market will tend towards full employment since as wages fall employers will be encouraged to recruit more labour and, according to Say's Law, production creates sufficient income to allow all goods produced to be purchased. Aggregate demand cannot therefore be deficient as it is a passive, dependent variable which *responds* to changes in aggregate supply. Some contemporary economists are referred to as 'supply-siders' as they support the views of the classical economists that aggregate supply is the dominant and independent variable.

The Keynesian view

In the Keynesian model the role of aggregate demand is far more important as it is seen as the independent variable which *causes* changes in aggregate supply. It is argued that the firms are motivated to produce by the level of aggregate demand and, in the event of a fall in demand, they will reduce their workforce and unemployment will follow. Unemployment is considered as involuntary since there is no inherent tendency towards full employment as firms are only willing to employ workers to produce sufficient to match aggregate demand. Whatever action the individual firm may take, e.g. reduce the desired wage rate, will not create employment.

The establishment
of equilibrium

For equilibrium to be established in the Keynesian model, it is necessary for planned expenditures (aggregate demand) to equal planned outputs (aggregate supply). Aggregate demand has four main components: consumption (C), investment (I), government expenditure (G) and net

foreign trade $(X - M)$. Changes in any of these will activate equal
changes in aggregate supply to establish a different level of national
income equilibrium. Aggregate supply can be represented by the income
generated from planned national output which is either spent on
consumption (C) or saved (S) or paid in taxes (T).

An additional feature of equilibrium is that injections into the flow of
income are equal to withdrawals. It must be remembered that equilibrium
in the Keynesian model does not necessarily mean full employment: it can
be established at any level of national income regardless of the level of
unemployment.

Changes in
equilibrium

An understanding of the *multiplier process* is essential to explain how
changes in aggregate expenditure will affect the level of national
income. The multiplier is activated by a change in any component of
national expenditure which causes an immediate increase in national
income since one person's spending is another person's income. The
process will continue in an infinite number of successive rounds in which
the expenditure generated will diminish since a proportion of income is
saved, taxed or spent on imports at each stage. The reciprocal of the
marginal propensity to withdraw is in fact the multiplier factor.

Government policy

The implication of the Keynesian model to government policy is that the
power to correct involuntary unemployment is in the hands of the
authorities. By stimulating the economy through an autonomous increase
in expenditure, the multiplier process will be activated and an increase
in aggregate demand will reduce the deflationary gap. This gap is the
difference between the present level and the desired level of aggregate
demand to ensure full employment. In the event that present aggregate
demand exceeds the full employment level, an inflationary gap exists
which can be corrected by an autonomous reduction in expenditure.

The weaknesses of the
Keynesian model

The reality of Keynesian demand management policy in the 1960s and 1970s
was of a 'stop-go' cycle of budgetary policy which had a very
destabilising influence. In addition, the Keynesian view has not
adequately explained the tendency in the 1970s for 'stagflation' or the
role of monetary changes and the behaviour of financial institutions.

EXERCISES

Exercise 1

Mix and match

A. Marginal propensity to consume

B. Average propensity to consume

C. Full employment

D. Pigou effect

E. Injection

F. Withdrawal

G. Autonomous expenditure

H. Induced expenditure

1. The increase in consumption which is brought about by a £1 increase in national income.

2. The level of consumption as a proportion of income at a given level of national income.

3. The changes in the real value of wealth resulting from changes in the price level.

4. Expenditure which will take place regardless of the level of national income.

5. Expenditure which will be determined by the level of national income.

6. Any part of national income not passed on within the circular flow.

7. All productive resources within an economy are in use.

8. Any addition to the circular flow which does not come from expenditure of domestic households.

Exercise 2

Practical exercises

An economy is closed to foreign trade, and the data in Table 18.1 is currently available for national income aggregates:

C = £2,000 m. + 0.5Y

I = £500 m.

G = £1,000 m.

T = 0.3Y

Table 18.1

Y	C	I	G	AD	Y	C	S	T	AS
0									
1,000									
2,000									
3,000									
4,000									
5,000									
6,000									
7,000									
8,000									
9,000									
10,000									

National income and employment

(a) Complete Table 18.1

(b) What is the correct function for savings in this model?

(c) What is the equilibrium level of national income?

(d) What are the features which distinguish equilibrium from other levels of income?

(e) Plot the relationship between aggregate demand and national income on a 45-degree line diagram.

(f) Immediately beneath the above diagram, plot the relationship between withdrawals (saving and tax) and national income and the relationship between injections (investment and government expenditure) and national income.

(g) If the government estimates the full employment level of national income to be at £8,000m., are there unemployed resources in the economy at present?

(h) What policy measures would you advocate to correct the present problem?

(i) What is the value of the multiplier?

(j) Calculate the required change in government expenditure to cause national income to change to the full employment level.

(k) What factors in practice make the operation of this model more difficult?

Exercise 3
Short-answer
questions

1. How will a fall in the proportion of savings to national income influence the value of the multiplier? What effect would this have on a given increase in autonomous investment?

2. A closed economy with no public sector is at full employment. $C = £1,000$ m. $+ 0.6Y$, $I = £1,500$m. What is the current level of national income? If autonomous consumption at all levels of national income fell by 20 per cent, what would be the new level of national income and how would this affect employment?

3. 'Since planned injections must equal planned withdrawals at equilibrium and that savings is a withdrawal and investment is an injection, savings must therefore equal investment at equilibrium.' Would you agree? Give reasons.

4. Draw diagrams to illustrate the effect of: (a) an increase in tax and (b) a decrease in public expenditure, on an economy with an inflationary gap.

5. Fig. 18.1 illustrates an economy which would generate Y(FE) national income at full employment. Does the economy have a deflationary or inflationary gap? Identify the correct letter

National income and employment

references for the appropriate gap.

Fig. 18.1

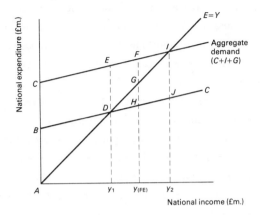

6. An economy is closed to foreign trade, $C = 0.75Yd$, $T = 0.2Y$. The government has authorised an additional £100m. expenditure (E) to reduce unemployment as part of its demand management strategy. Table 18.2 sets out the multiplier process in stages.

Using Table 18.2 complete the next two rounds of the multiplier process.

What would be the eventual totals for each column at infinity?

Table 18.2

	E	Y	T	C	S
Round 1	100	100	20	60	20
Round 2	60				
Round 3					
Total at infinity					

7. What factors determine the level of savings in the economy?

Exercise 4

Data response

War is no Cure for Inflation

In 1932 the average rate of unemployment in Britain was 22%. By 1939 it was down to 10% and the economy was booming at least partly as a result of rearmament. Should we conclude from this that war, or the threat of war, is no bad thing for economies facing recession?

Although wars and rumours of war can have enormous economic effects they are never an optimal economic policy. Increasing defence expenditure, whether the weapons are actually used or not, distorts the supply side of the economy. Money spent on defence tends to be poorer value than money spent by consumers. The defence spin off argument is largely bogus. One or two discoveries made in the course of military research may have civilian applications but this is a matter of chance. Arguably Britain's defence industry has been a source of weakness to the economy over the post-war years rather than a source of strength.

The impact of rearmament on demand is ambiguous - making guns after all is better than being unemployed, and money in the pockets of defence workers finds its way into every other sector of the economy. Extra spending on defence will only be expansionary if it is financed in an inflationary manner, it may not add to demand if extra borrowing is funded by bond issues. Suppose it is financed by money creation, the extra spending will then add to demand and may increase output. But it will increase output only at the expense of inflation. Relaxation of the fiscal and monetary reins to finance a Middle East war would end any chance of progress on inflation. The Korean war was a good example of the inflationary fallout from a large scale conflict. The cost was piled on top of a world economy stretched by the demands of post-second world war reconstruction and the result was a commodity boom and a rapid rise in inflation. Even in the Thirties rearmament was hardly an optimal solution to recession. A big road or school building programme might have been equally effective in reducing unemployment.

More important is the immediate question of what effect the rise in the oil price and the reversion of sterling to petrocurrency status may have. The CBI's latest forecast shows more or less zero growth for the next four quarters based on the assumption of an average oil price of $24 per barrel.

An extract from *The Times* 28th August 1990

(a) In what respects would an increase in defence expenditure distort the supply side of the economy?

(b) Evaluate alternative ways in which an increase in defence expenditure could be financed.

National income and employment

(c) Using appropriate diagrams explain how a big road building programme could reduce unemployment in a recession.

(d) What effects would a rise in oil prices to $30 per barrel and the reversion of sterling to the status of a petrocurrency have on the Uk economy?

Exercise 5

Essay questions

1. Since national expenditure always equals national output by definition, then the economy must always be in equilibrium. Discuss.

2. Unemployment may not solely be due to inadequate aggregate demand. Discuss.

3. 'An increase in savings is a pre-requisite of a faster rate of economic growth.' 'An increase in savings will cause incomes to fall.' Can these two statements be reconciled?

4. Explain how the multiplier works in an economy which has no public sector and no involvement in foreign trade. How does the introduction of these two dimensions of the model affect the operation of the multiplier?

5. Contrast the Keynesian and classical approaches to the achievement of full employment.

Exercise 6

Group discussion

It has been widely reported that despite the current high levels of unemployment, serious skill shortages exist especially in engineering and information technology. The discussion takes place at a board meeting of a medium-sized engineering company located in Reading. The personnel director has reported to the meeting that the response to recent local advertising for engineering apprentices was three applicants for fifteen places.

1. Why has the response to the local adverts been so low?
2. Would an advertising campaign in another part of the country be more successful?
3. Should the firm try to recruit qualified engineers instead of training their own apprentices?
4. What policy measures should be taken by government to encourage workers into engineering?
5. Is it the responsibility of the state or private industry to train engineering apprentices? Which should bear the cost?

ANSWERS

Exercise 1

Mix and match   A. 1   B. 2   C. 7   D. 3

                        E. 8   F. 6   G. 4   H. 5

Exercise 2

Practical exercise

(b) $S = -2,000 + 0.2Y$

(c) £7,000m

(g) £1,000m

(i) 2

(j) + £500m

Exercise 4

Data response

(a) Supply side could be distorted by transfer of productive resources into direct state control and away from the market economy.

(b) 1. Increase in PSBR funded by sale of gilt-edged stock.

      This would not be inflationary as the funding would be drawn largely from private sector savings on a long term basis.

    2. Increase taxation.

      Would reduce the level of domestic consumption and reduce investment in the longer term. Would therefore tend to depress the economy.

    3. Borrow from Bank of England and banking sector.

      Would tend to increase the money supply and be inflationary. May also have an effect on short term interest rates.

(c)

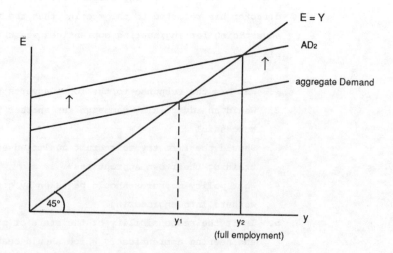

National income and employment

(d) A high oil price tends to increase demand for sterling as the UK is
an oil producer. This causes a rise in the sterling exchange rate
which is likely to adversely affect the Balance of Payments. The UK
is however a substantial oil importer and higher costs may increase
inflation. There may be some negative effect on inflation as supply
prices of imported materials would be less at a higher exchange rate.

Exercise 5

Essay questions   1.

* A distinction must be drawn between *planned* income and expenditure
and *actual* income and expenditure.

* In an accounting sense, the statement is true as accounts are drawn
up from historic data.

* The economy is not in equilibrium until planned injections equal
planned withdrawals.

* There is nothing special about equilibrium as the economy may be in
equilibrium at any level of national income. What policy makers are
concerned with is the full employment equilibrium.

19 Consumption and investment

Together, consumption and investment account for more than 75 per cent of the national expenditure and changes in either will therefore have a major impact on the economy. This chapter analyses some of the conflicting views on the factors which determine these aggregates and what causes them to change.

Consumption

The Keynesian model assumes that whatever the level of income, some autonomous consumption must take place for subsistence. This is represented by the intercept of the consumption function. The increases in consumption above this subsistence level will be in direct proportion to increases in disposable income. The *marginal propensity to consume* determines this proportion and it is represented by the gradient of the consumption function. For the UK between 1946 and 1980 the consumption function has been estimated as:

$$C = 2,634 \text{ (thousand million)} + 0.666Y$$

$$\text{(intercept)} \qquad\qquad \text{(gradient)}$$

Thus Keynesian view is often referred to as the *absolute income hypothesis*. Empirical evidence has led to recent criticism of this view, particularly long-run time-series data which suggests the average propensity to consume is remarkably stable despite significant long-run variations in income. The most well-known alternative to the absolute income hypothesis is the *permanent income hypothesis* advanced by Friedman. This view suggests that all households have a long-run level of income which is determined by social class background, expected lifetime earnings and accumulated wealth. Current income may deviate significantly from the permanent income in the short run. For example, an accountant's son reading law at university may have a high permanent income but a low current income. The difference is referred to as transitory income. Household's current expenditure is said to be determined by permanent income, and short-run transitory income will have little influence. Long-run consumption plans will be maintained by savings and dis-savings. The *relative income hypothesis* again challenges the relationship between consumption and current income by suggesting that the household's relative income is more important. Relative income relates current income to past standards of living and to the consumption levels of friends and relatives.

Investment

The contemporary debate on investment tends to centre on the relative importance of variables which determine investment. The classical view stresses the *rate of interest* as the key variable. It is supported by the evidence of widely used investment appraisal techniques which are highly interest elastic, e.g. discounted cash flow. Empirical research

Consumption and investment

suggests that this relationship is in fact rather weak as small changes
in interest rates have little effect on investment decisions. The
accelerator principle relates current investment with the rate of change
of national income. Firms will invest if their current capacity is
insufficient to match anticipated future demand. A further factor which
is regarded as of great importance is business expectations but this is,
of course, impossible to quantify.

EXERCISES

Exercise 1

Mix and match

A. Transitory income

B. Permanent income

C. Relative income

D. Accelerator

E. Net present value

F. Average propensity to save

G. Marginal efficiency of investment

H. Marginal propensity to save

1. The proportion of net income earned by domestic
   households not passed on into expenditures within
   the circular flow.

2. Short-term unexpected changes in a household's
   income.

3. The relationship between the level of investment
   and the growth rate of output.

4. The current value of future benefits and outlays
   from investment alternatives.

5. The proportion of additional net income earned by
   domestic households which is not passed on into
   expenditures within the circular flow.

6. The earning power of the last increment of
   capital invested.

7. The present value of expected flows of income and
   wealth over a long period of time.

8. A household's income in relation to incomes of
   peers, relatives and neighbours.

Exercise 2

Practical exercise

Discounted cash flow and marginal efficiency of capital. A company is
considering an investment project which requires a £20,000 capital outlay
now and is expected to generate year-end net cash inflows for the next
five years as shown. There is no scrap value for the equipment and the
effects of inflation are ignored.

Year	Net cash inflow (£)
1	4,000
2	5,000
3	9,000
4	5,000
5	5,000

Consumption and investment

(a) Calculate the net present value of the investment at the following rates of interest; (i) 5 per cent; (ii) 10 per cent; (iii) 15 per cent.

(b) What do you observe about the behaviour of the NPV as the rate of interest is increased?

(c) Complete Table 19.1.

Table 19.1

Rate of interest (%)	5%	6%	7%	8%	9%	10%	11%	12%	13%	14%	15%
NPV (£)											

(d) Graph the relationship between NPV and the rate of interest using the horizontal scale for interest rates.

(e) At what rate of interest is the NPV equal to zero?

(f) What is the relationship between rates of interest and approval of investment decisions for this company?

(g) If an alternative investment opportunity was available which required a £20,000 capital outlay with net cash inflows as shown below, which would represent the best use of the firm's funds?

Year	Net inflows (£)
1	6,000
2	6,000
3	4,000
4	4,000
5	10,000

Exercise 3
Short-answer
questions

1. What does the consumption function $C = 2,000 + 0.75Y$ tell you about the level of consumption at different levels of national income? What is the corresponding savings function?

2. If the consumption function was expressed as $C = 2,000 + 0.75Yd$, whatis the difference between this and the above function? What is this consumption function in relation to Y if $T = 0.25Y$?

Consumption and investment

3. If the consumption functon is non-linear, how will this affect the marginal propensity to consume?

4. What is being shown in Fig. 19.1 by *NP/ON*?

Fig. 19.1

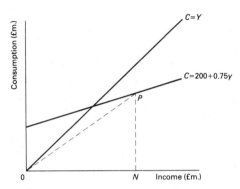

5. Draw a consumption function in which MPC = APC at all levels of national income.

6. What factors are likely to explain a rightward shift of the MEI function as shown Fig. 19.2?

Fig. 19.2

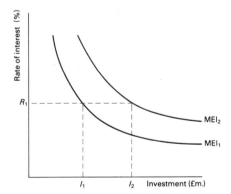

Exercise 4

Data response

(a) What is the difference between figures expressed as 1985 prices (as in Table 19.2) and figures expressed as current prices?

(b) How would these figures need to be adjusted to more accurately reflect the change in capital formation in the UK economy in one year?

Table 19.2   Revised figures. Gross Domestic Fixed Capital Formation

£ million at 1985 prices

	1978	1979	1980	1981	1982	1983	1984	1985	1986	1987	1988
Private sector:											
Vehicles, ships and aircraft	6 343	6 540	5 119	4 209	4 479	4 434	5 310	5 657	5 148	6 078	6 949
Plant and machinery	13 204	14 480	14 406	13 199	13 521	13 796	16 158	20 072	20 368	21 982	26 659
Dwellings[2]	8 864	9 665	9 134	8 149	8 680	9 323	9 737	9 323	10 347	11 074	12 212
Other new buildings and works	6 981	6 895	6 486	6 418	6 616	6 560	7 504	7 786	8 124	10 532	11 782
Purchases *less* sales of land and existing buildings	2 745	2 619	3 359	3 838	5 544	4 972	5 163	5 149	5 137	5 890	6 820
National accounts statistical adjustment[3]	-	-	-	-	-	-	-	-	-	-	850
Total	38 307	40 268	38 577	35 990	38 892	39 085	43 872	47 987	49 124	55 556	65 272
Public corporations:											
Vehicles, ships and aircraft	629	737	937	488	355	502	614	590	424	364	401
Plant and machinery	4 338	4 447	4 390	4 311	4 177	4 613	4 032	2 579	2 322	2 115	2 117
Dwellings[2]	403	447	419	339	333	354	327	280	234	237	211
Other new buildings and works	3 306	3 039	3 013	2 729	3 128	3 197	2 950	2 703	2 697	2 376	2 350
Purchases *less* sales of land and existing buildings	-1	46	-240	-53	-118	-176	-350	-380	-361	-726	-606
Total	8 686	8 677	8 491	7 775	7 906	8 490	7 573	5 772	5 316	4 366	4 473
General government:											
Vehicles, ships and aircraft	177	235	240	198	194	241	208	189	179	162	152
Plant and machinery	768	790	842	755	764	992	1 030	1 214	1 287	1 237	1 341
Dwellings[2]	3 488	3 168	2 778	1 817	1 949	2 570	2 498	2 256	2 302	2 504	2 379
Other new buildings and works	3 845	3 836	3 570	3 352	4 066	4 121	4 715	4 722	4 978	4 946	4 666
Purchases *less* sales of land and existing buildings	-240	-362	-950	-1 491	-2 905	-2 023	-1 838	-1 797	-1 708	-1 877	-2 603
Total	7 684	7 349	6 290	4 632	4 313	5 901	6 613	6 584	7 038	6 972	5 935
Total	54 914	56 450	53 416	48 298	50 915	53 476	58 058	60 343	61 478	66 894	75 680

Source: National Income and Expenditure Accounts 1989 (HMSO)

(c) What factors might account for (1) the dramatic fall in private sector investment in 1980 and 1981, (2) the dramatic rise in private sector investment in 1987/8?

(d) How would factors which determine private sector investment differ from those which determine public sector investment?

Exercise 5

Essay questions

1. 'Investment incentives seem to have failed in the UK as our rate of new investment is still too low both in relation to our own needs and compared with our principal competitors.' How far can government influence the level of investment in the UK economy?

2. What do you understand by the expression 'propensity to consume' and what are its principal determinants?

3. 'Savings in short enriches and spending impoverishes the community along with the individual' (J.S. Mill). How far would you agree with this statement?

4. To what extent has empirical research discredited the Keynesian view that consumption expenditure is directly related to current income?

5. Examine the effects of inflation on the levels of savings and investment.

Exercise 6

Group discussion

Fig. 19.3

Major Industrial Countries: Household Saving Rates, 1970-1989 Q1[1]
(Proportion of disposable income)

Average					1988			
	1970-79	1980	1984	1988 Q1	Q2	Q3	Q4
Canada	10.3	13.3	14.8	9.2	8.5	8.6	9.8	9.9
United States	8.2	7.1	6.2	4.2	4.4	3.7	4.2	4.3
Japan	21.0	17.9	16.0	15.0[2] ...	...	...	...
France	13.9	12.7	14.6	12.3	12.2	12.8	12.1	12.1
Germany, Fed.Rep.of	14.6	14.0	12.8	13.6	13.2	13.7	13.5	13.9
Italy	....	....	22.6	19.1	....	....	....	....
United Kingdom	10.6	13.9	10.5	4.5	4.7	5.2	2.9	5.1
Average excluding								
Italy	12.9	11.9	10.8	8.9	6.8	...	...	...

[1] Average of individual countries weighted by the U.S. dollar value of their respective GNPs in 1988.

[2] Fiscal year 1987 (April 1987-March 1988)

Source: *World Economic Outlook* IMF 1989

1. Discuss the possible explanations for the trends in personal sector savings evident in Fig. 19.3.

2. Should parents encourage their children to save?

3. What would you expect to be the relationship between savings and inflation?

4. What effect would the decrease in personal sector savings have on the value of the muliplier, employment and aggregate demand?

5. Is the current pattern of household savings in the U.K. to the advantage or disadvantage of the U.K. economy in comparison to other countries shown?

ANSWERS

Exercise 1

Mix and match

A. 2   B. 7   C. 8   D. 3

E. 4   F. 1   G. 6   H. 5

Exercise 2

Practical exercise   (a)   (i) NPV at 5 per cent = + 4,149

Consumption and investment

(ii) NPV at 10 per cent = + 1,048

(iii) NPV at 15 per cent = - 1,478

(b) NPV falls as R is increased

(c)

				Rate of interest (%)						
5	6	7	8	9	10	11	12	13	14	15
4,149	3,475	2,830	2,212	1,619	1,048	503	-22	-527	-1,012	-1,480

(e) 11.8 per cent (approx.)

(f) Project approval is more likely at lower interest rates

(g) Project A: IRR = 11.8 per cent

Project B: IRR = 14.28 per cent.

Exercise 4

Data response

(a) 1980 prices represent figures which have been adjusted for the changes in money values due to inflation.

(b) Capital depreciation on existing investment stock should be deducted.

(c)

* Adverse influence on business expectations of rising unemployment.

* Higher rates of interest.

* Negative accelerator due to a reduction in the rate of change of national income.

* Possible 'crowding out' by public sector borrowing.

(d)

* Public sector investment determined by macroeconomic policy, e.g. PSBR restraint, constraint on money supply growth.

* Public sector investment can be used as a counter-cyclical influence on aggregate demand.

* Public investment may be determined by social costs and benefits identified by cost-benefit analysis.

Exercise 5

Essay questions

1.

* Public sector investment determined by government policy on PSBR, local authority rates and monetary constraints.

* Tax incentives can be given through capital allowances against corporation tax.

* Business expectations can be partially formed by government economic policy.

* Monetary policy may significantly influence availability of investment finance.

Consumption and investment

*   Government intervention into money markets will influence rates of
    interest.

It must be stressed that government can only encourage business
investment, the principal determining factor being the level of expected
future demand.

20 Money I

Assets classified as 'money' must fulfil both *medium of exchange* and *store of wealth* functions; functions which imply general acceptability in transactions and the absence of capital risk. While any meaningful definition of money must include bank notes and coin, there exists a whole range of capital certain liquid assets, such as interest-bearing bank and building society deposits, which can quickly and easily be converted into cash with only minimal penalty. The UK monetary authorities are naturally concerned with definitions of money which relate closely to money national income, but the existence of many close substitutes for interest-bearing bank deposits has led to the monitoring of money supply growth on various definitions, including £M3, M4 and the officially targeted M0.

The money market: Bank of England, commercial banks and the discount houses

In order to appreciate monetary developments and policy measures it is necessary to know something about the activities of the financial institutions operating in the money market and the relationships that exist between them.

Besides its note issue function and its responsibility for the supervision of the banking system, the *Bank of England* acts as banker for both commercial banks and the government. The Bank is also responsible for implementing the government's monetary policies and the management of the national debt.

The *discount houses* can be regarded as intermediaries between the Bank of England and the commercial banks. Their main business is the discounting of commercial and Treasury bills and they serve an important function in the channelling of surplus funds from some banks to those that are short of cash. If the banks are generally short of cash and call back loans made to the discount houses, then the latter are able to obtain cash quickly through the 'lender of last resort' facility offered by the Bank of England. The Bank will purchase bills from the discount houses to relieve the cash shortage, but will do so at discount rates designed to prevent any excessive growth of the money supply.

The banks and credit creation

The *commercial banks* only need to keep a relatively small proportion of their deposits in the form of cash reserves and since 1981 bank prudence has dictated the ratio of cash reserves to deposit liabilities. Since a large fraction of any increase in bank deposits can be loaned out to customers and most of this lending simply swells total bank deposits, further loans are clearly possible. The extent of the credit creation possibilities is obviously influenced by the prudential cash ratios observed by banks but the scope is reduced by various leakages which reduce the volume of bank deposits, e.g. an increased demand for cash by the public.

Changes in the money supply and monetary control measures

Besides changes in the public's demand for cash, there are several other sources of change in the money supply. These include changes in net currency flows overseas, changes in the banks' desired cash reserve ratios and changes in both the private and public sectors' demand for bank loans. Currently the government's main monetary control measures include the Bank of England's bill market operations, whereby it influences the level of short-term interest rates in the money market, and fiscal policy. The latter is concerned with controlling the size of the PSBR and thus the pressure on money supply growth and interest rates. Concern over the relationship between the size of the PSBR, the growth of the money supply and the level of interest rates prompted the introduction of the medium-term financial strategy in March 1980.

The medium-term financial strategy (MTFS)

By announcing targets for £M3 growth and the PSBR over a 4-year period the government's intention was to bring down the rate of inflation quickly by influencing the public's inflation expectations and creating favourable circumstances for sustained economic growth. However, £M3 grew by 20 per cent in 1980 and was giving an unreliable picture of the underlying monetary conditions following the termination of the 'corset' in June 1980 and the consequent re-intermediation of funds. This experience led to the abandonment of £M3 as a targeted monetary aggregate in 1986 and more attention was then paid to narrow definitions of money, in particular M0. There is clearly no simple link between any official definition of money and the inflationary process. The emphasis of economic policy has more recently moved towards the use of interest rates to manipulate consumer spending and the value of sterling rather than targeted monetary aggregates. This has been necessary in view of the growing Balance of Payments deficit and the pre-conditions laid down for Britain's entry into the European Monetary System.

EXERCISES

Exercise 1

Mix and match

A. M4 Money definition

B. Trade bill

1. That part of the money supply which is under the direct control of the monetary authorities.

2. All bank deposits of less than £100,000 and building society deposits, both withdrawable within one month.

C. Monetary base

D. Special deposits

E. Open market operations

F. Treasury bill

G. Retail depositis

H. Credit creation

3. £M3 plus Building society shares, deposits and Certificates of deposit minus holdings of bank deposits by building societies.

4. An instrument of short-term borrowing by the government.

5. An instrument of short-term borrowing by industrial and commercial companies.

6. Deposits which banks are sometimes required to lodge with the Bank of England, earn interest at Treasury bill rate, and cause a reduction in the volume of banks' liquid assets.

7. The process by which an initial increase in bank deposits leads to a much larger increase in total bank deposits.

8. A method of controlling the money supply via the sales and purchases of government securities by the Bank of England.

Exercise 2

Practical exercise   *Credit creation.* The table below shows the initial change in the balance sheet of an economy's only commercial bank following an increase in government spending:-

	(£B) Liabilities		(£B) Assets	
Stage 1	Deposits	100	Cash	5
			Loans	95
		100		100
Stage 2	Deposits	102	Cash	7
			Loans	95
		102		102

Notes

1. The bank observes a prudential cash ratio of 5 per cent - i.e. desired ratio of cash to deposits = 5 per cent - and there is no requirement by the central bank for the bank to hold non-operational cash balances.

2. All funds loaned by the bank remain within the banking system, i.e. no leakages of deposits which must imply a fixed demand for cash by the public.

3. Deposits are the only bank liabilities and cash and loans the only bank assets.

(a) By taking the balance sheet adjustment process 2 stages further on, illustrate the principle of credit creation and briefly explain the adjustments.

(b) Determine the value of the bank credit multiplier and thus the new equilibrium level of bank deposits when adjustment is completed.

(c) It is rather unrealistic to suggest that there are no leakages of deposits. For example, the public may wish to increase their cash holdings in direct proportion to the level of bank deposits. If the public's desired cash ratio - i.e. ratio of cash to deposits - was equal to 10 per cent, then how would this change the extent of credit creation in the above example?

Hint

Consider the following identities and incorporate the assumptions concerning both the public's and the bank's cash holdings into these identities for the purpose of deriving an equation which relates

D to B:

$B = C + R$

$M = C + D$

where

B = monetary base

C = public's cash holdings

R = bank's cash holdings

D = bank deposits

M = money supply.

Exercise 3

Short-answer questions

1. Briefly outline the monetary control arrangements introduced by the Bank of England in August 1981.

2. Explain the significance of the Bank of England's 'lender of last resort' function.

3. With the aid of an example, explain the process of credit creation.

4. In the *Bank of England Quarterly Bulletin* there is a table of figures relating to official operations of the Bank in the money markets. Briefly explain the nature and purpose of the 'purchase and resale agreements' in relation to bills.

5. If banks find themselves short of cash for their desired volume of lending, how are they likely to react and what will happen to money market interest rates and the size of the monetary base?

6. What is the likely impact on the money supply of a net transfer of funds from interest-bearing bank deposit accounts to building society deposit accounts and what factors might prompt such a transfer?

7. Explain the relationship between the growth of the money supply, the PSBR and interest rates according to the Treasury view.

Money - I

Data response

Table 20.1 Selected Economic Indicators for the U.K. (figures in £bn)

	1985/6	1986/7	1987/8	1988/9	1989/90
GDP at current market prices	361.9	388.4	430.3	478.4	519.2
PSBR	5.7	3.6	-3,4	-14.5	-7.7
Money Stock MD	14.2	14.8	15.5	16.6	17.5
Money Stock M4	236.1	270.5	315.9	372.7	438.8
BOP. Current Account	4.8	-1.0	-7.9	-15.9	-19.5
Sterling Exchange Rate (1985 = 100)	100.5	89.5	91.8	96.4	90.4
3 mth interback Interest Rate (%)	12.09	10.51	9.3	11.32	14.42
Retail Price Index (Jan 1987 = 100)	-	-	103.3	111.0	119.5

Source: *Financial Statistics* July 1990

The following questions are based on the figures in Table 20.1.

(a) What factors have influenced the level of money market interest rates, as represented by the 3 month interbank rate, over the period shown?

(b) What are the monetary implications of a negative Public Sector Borrowing Requirement?

(c) What conclusions can be drawn from the figures on the effectiveness of a high interest rates policy to control the macro-economy.

(d) What policy measures would you recommend to correct the Balance of Payments deficit?

Exercise 5

Essay questions

1. Describe the main methods employed by the UK monetary authorities, since 1981, to control the money supply, explaining briefly how they work in principle. Have they been successful?

2. 'Announcing firm medium-term monetary targets is a mistake.' Discuss this statement in the light of UK experience in the 1980s.

3. Carefully explain the likely impact on UK banks of the following:

   (a) A sharp fall in oil prices.

   (b) An improvement in business confidence in the UK.

   (c) An increase in money market interest rates.

   (d) A reduced demand for notes and coin by the public.

Exercise 6

Group discussion

What is money and what is not? The monetary authorities publish detailed statistics on a variety of money supply and liquidity measures. In the 1980s they have targeted several different definitions of 'money', changing their mind on the most appropriate definitions for targeting purposes. There appears to be some confusion as to what 'money' really should include which raises questions concerning the key criteria governing the selection of financial assets which should constitute 'money'.

Points of interest for discussion are:

1. For what purpose(s) are we defining groups of financial assets as constituting 'money'?

2. Would the focus of attention on a single monetary aggregate ultimately render the particular definition redundant from a policy point of view?

ANSWERS

Exercise 1

Mix and match

A. 3	B. 5	C. 1	D. 6
E. 8	F. 4	G. 2	H. 7

Exercise 2

Practical exercise   (a)

	£B Liabilities	£B Assets
Stage 3	Deposits 103.9	Cash 7
		Loans 96.9
	103.9	103.9
Stage 4	Deposits 105.705	Cash 7
		Loans 98.705
	105.705	105.705

Stage 3 sees a creation of credit as bank assets and liabilities have now risen by more than the original £2bn. increase in deposits. At stage 2, the bank was holding excess cash - it only needed to hold £5.1bn. cash and therefore was able to lend the other £1.9bn. This lending immediately swells bank deposits by £1.9bn. since there are, by assumption, no leakages. At stage 3 the bank still holds surplus cash and is able to lend another £1.805bn. which represents 95 per cent of the £1.9bn. increase in deposits between stages 2 and 3. So at stage 4, total liabilities and assets rise to £105.705bn. The adjustments will continue until the desired cash ratio is restored.

(b) Bank credit multiplier = reciprocal of cash reserve ratio

$$= \frac{100}{5} = \underline{20} \text{ in this example.}$$

New equilibrium value of bank deposits = 20 x 7 = £140 billion.

(c) The relevant multiplier now becomes $\frac{100}{5+10} = 6.67$

Starting from the same initial position, where the bank has £100bn. deposits, the new credit creation power following an initial increase in deposits of £2bn. is somewhat reduced as the substantial fall in the value of the bank credit multiplier shows.

New level of deposits = 100 + (2 x 6.67) = £113.34bn.

Exercise 5

Essay questions   1.

* Note the various definitions of money, mentioning the officially targeted MO and £M3.

* Point out that the monetary authorities aim to achieve medium-term control of £M3 and short-term control of MO.

* Explanations of the Bank of England's bill market operations, the use of fiscal policy as an instrument of money supply control and overfunding are required.

* The success, or otherwise, of the control measures used requires a qualified answer. In relation to the original MTFS, the methods employed appear to have been unsuccessful, but were the targets set necessarily appropriate?

21 Money II

Effective control over inflation requires the existence and correct identification by the government of a stable *demand for money* function in addition to the ability to achieve the money supply targets set. With regard to the behaviour of £M3 in the 1980s and the rate of inflation experienced, it would appear that the public's demand for money behaviour has been far from predictable. The relationship between the money supply and the average level of prices is a key concern for monetary policy.

The quantity theory of money and the Cambridge equation

The equation $MV = PT$ is merely an identity stating that the total quantity of money handed over in transactions is equal to the value of goods sold. However, since the classical economists believed that market forces would keep the economy at, or near to, full employment and that institutional factors, such as frequency of wage and salary payments, were slow to change, it followed that in the short run T (the volume of transactions) and V (the velocity of circulation of money) are effectively constants. From this follows the proposition that the average price level is directly proportional to the quantity of money in circulation.

The Cambridge equation ($M^D = KPy = KY$) is specifically expressed as a demand for money relationship in which the public's money-holdings are related to income. After allowing for the facts that only final market transactions were thought to be relevant, as opposed to all market transactions, and that the stock of money is willingly held by the public in equilibrium, the equation can be regarded as a reformulation of the quantity theory identity with $K = 1/V$.

The Keynesian theory of money

Keynes identified motives for holding money and his essential contribution was the development of the asset or speculative demand for money. The public could move between bonds (capital risky assets) and money, and would do so according to expectations regarding movements in bond prices (interest rates are inversely related). The demand for money was held to be interest-elastic on account of this speculative motive and the rate of interest was determined by the interaction of the money supply, determined by the monetary authorities, and the public's total demand for money. It follows from the sensitivity of money demand to the rate of interest that a substantial change in the money supply would be required to significantly influence market rates of interest in the absence of demand curve shifts prompted by possible changes in speculative behaviour. Since it is via interest rates that money supply changes were believed to have their major thrust on the goods market and since Keynes believed that both investment and consumption were interest-inelastic, the clear implication is that monetary policy is unlikely to have a significant influence on output and employment. Finally, Keynesians have held that the speculative motive is responsible for considerable instability in the public's money-holding behaviour which implies that the correlation between money supply growth and changes in the national income is likely to be weak.

The modern quantity theory and the monetarists

The monetarist view is that the demand for real money balances is influenced by wealth rather than current income, and the expected rates of return on the various forms of wealth. Unlike Keynesian theory which suggests that the demand for money is interest-elastic, monetarists believe that it has a low interest-elasticity since money is not merely a substitute for bonds but rather for a whole range of assets including physical goods.

Following an increase in the money supply, excess money balances will be spent on both financial assets and physical goods so that in contrast to the Keynesian case there will be a direct stimulus to output and prices. Since monetarists also believe that the demand for money function is inherently stable, they expect money supply changes to have a predictable impact on aggregate demand and inflation after allowing for market expectation and adjustment lags.

EXERCISES

Exercise 1

Mix and match

A. Income velocity of circulation of money

B. Interest-elasticity of demand for money

C. The real demand for money

D. Liquidity preference theory of interest

E. Speculative demand for money

F. Liquidity trap

1. Ratio of money national income to the money stock.

2. The Keynesian notion that the supply of and demand for money determine the market rate of interest.

3. The public's holdings of idle balances which vary in accordance with the expected return on capital risky financial assets.

4. The sensitivity of the public's moneyholdings to changes in the rate of interest.

5. Any increase in the supply of money is willingly held by the public in the form of idle balances as nobody believes that the prices of capital risky financial assets will rise.

6. Public's money holdings deflated by an index measuring movements in the average level of prices.

Exercise 2

Short-answer
questions

1. According to the quantity theory of money, a 5 per cent increase in
   the money supply would result in a 5 per cent increase in the average
   level of prices. Explain.

2. If at current market rates of interest there was an upward revision
   by the public of the 'normal' rate of interest, what impact would
   this have on the demand for money? Briefly explain.

3. Briefly outline the Keynesian view regarding the likely impact of an
   increase in the money supply on the level of economic activity.

4. What is meant by the term 'demand for money function'?

5. What influence would an anticipated increase in inflation be expected
   to have on (a) the demand for narrow money, and (b) the demand for
   broad money?

6. Under what set of circumstances might a 'liquidity trap' situation
   exist?

Exercise 3

Data response

Table 21.1 Money stock and velocity of circulation - UK

| | (£B) Amounts outstanding at end of period | | Velocity of circulation: ratios | |
	M1	£M3	M1	£M3
1982	40.2	91.5	7.60	3.23
1983	44.8	101.8	7.37	3.18
1984	51.8	112.1	6.66	3.08
1985	61.2	127.2	6.21	2.95

Source: *Financial Statistics*, May 1986

The following questions are based on Table 21.1:

(a) Does the information provided tend to support monetarist or Keynesian
    views regarding the stability of the public's demand for money
    behaviour? Would any other information be useful? Briefly explain.

(b) According to the information on £M3, what is the annual growth in
    money national income between the end of 1983 and the end of 1984?

(c) By reference to the *Financial Statistics Explanatory Handbook*,
    determine:

    (i) the definition of money national income to which the velocity
         of circulation ratios relate;

(ii) the reason for the apparent discrepancies between the M1-based
and £M3-based estimates of money national income which can be
derived from the information provided.

(d) Using the information on M1 explain, by reference to the quantity
theory of money, how the growth in national output could be
determined over the year 1985 if you are provided with the additional
information below:

	1984	1985
Average level of prices: index	100.0	105.5

(e) What explanations can be given for the fall in velocity of
circulation ratios over the period?

Exercise 4

Essay questions

1. 'Given that the monetary authorities in an economy can control the
money supply sufficiently closely, and have the political will to do
so, it must be the case that inflation targets will be realised.'
Discuss the validity, or otherwise, of this statement.

2. Compare and contrast Keynesian demand for money theory with
Friedman's modern quantity theory approach.

3. 'Sometimes the demand for money falls following an increase in
interest rates and sometimes it rises. Indeed, for different
definitions of money, both these responses may occur at the same
time.' Carefully consider these statements and come to a reasoned
conclusion on their validity.

Exercise 5

Group discussion

· *Is the public's money-holding behaviour essentially predictable and
related in a stable way to a few key economic variables?*

Group to be split into 'Keynesians' and 'monetarists' prior to the
discussion. Each school of thought required to make out the appropriate
case and to briefly present this, together with any relevant supporting
material, at the start of the discussion period. The ensuing discussion
should focus on UK monetary experience in the 1980s and the light this
can shed on the question. Finally, and most importantly, the policy
implications of both the Keynesian and monetarist views should be
examined.

ANSWERS

Exercise 1

Mix and match   A. 1   B. 4   C. 6   D. 2   E. 3   F. 5

Exercise 3

Data response

(a) Further information such as interest rate movements is required. However, it can be said that movements in the velocities of M1 and £M3 are not excessive and despite the gradual trend fall in the income velocity of M1 (probably due to the increase in the interest-bearing component of this aggregate) there is no evidence to support any serious instability. Some support for the monetarist line.

(b) $MV = Y$. Therefore, multiplying £M3 by its associated velocity will give money national income.

	1983	1984	% increase	1987	1988	% increase
Y	£324bn.	£345bn.	6.5	£441bn.	£488 bn.	10.54%

(c) i) GNP at current market prices.

   ii) The velocities relate annualised 4th quarter GNP to the average mid-month money stock figures for the 4th quarter of each year *and not the end of quarter figures* actually shown in the table.

(d) $MV = Py$

   Growth in M1 in 1985   = 18.1%

   % change in V in 1985 = -6.8%

   Inflation   = 5.5%   Given

   $MV = Py$ therefore $\dfrac{MV}{P} = y$

   $\therefore \dfrac{1.181 \times 0.932}{1.055} = 1.0433$ Approx 4.3%

(e) Degregulation of financial markets, more competition in the commercial banking sector, financial innovation, greater international integration of financial markets.

Exercise 4

Essay questions

1.

* Mention the fact that the authorities must be able to control a policy-relevant definition of money.

* Use the quantity theory identity to show that control of the money supply is not sufficient to guarantee close control over inflation.

* Note that Keynesians would take issue with the statement because of their views concerning velocity and the speculative demand for money.

* Subject to time-lags, Monetarists would consider the statement broadly valid as they believe the demand for money function to be essentially stable.

* An identified policy-relevant definition of money may not remain policy-relevant once the authorities attempt to control it.

22 Money and national income

Regarding the relationship between money and the level of economic activity, the IS-LM model provides a useful framework for comparing Keynesian, neoclassical and monetarist views. It takes the form of a simple macroeconomic model of the economy covering the goods and money markets. The impact of changes in aggregate demand and the money supply on the national income can usefully be explored using IS-LM analysis.

The goods and money markets - IS-LM analysis

The LM curve shows all those combinations of the rate of interest and the level of national income at which the monetary sector of the economy is in equilibrium. A graph of the LM curve, with the rate of interest on the vertical and national income on the horizontal axis, slopes upwards from left to right.

The IS curve shows all those combinations of the rate of interest and the level of national income at which the goods market is in equilibrium. When plotted on the same graph as the LM curve, it slopes downwards from left to right. A general equilibrium position is reached at the intersection of the IS and LM curves where both the money and goods markets are in equilibrium. The IS and LM curves will shift in response to changes in market circumstances: for example, an increase in the money supply would cause the LM curve to shift to the right while a sudden increase in savings would cause the IS curve to shift to the left.

Despite the usefulness of the IS-LM model, some criticisms are in order. For example, in its basic form the model cannot deal with time paths for market adjustment lags, and it does not enable us to examine the effects of changes in aggregate demand on *both* output and prices.

Keynesian and neo-classical economics

Unlike the Keynesians, neoclassical economists argue that the flexibility of money wages and prices ensures that the economy would always tend to full employment. However, even ignoring both the 'liquidity trap' and 'inflexible prices' arguments, Keynesians still claimed that if investment is highly interest-inelastic - i.e. a near vertical IS curve - an economy could suffer persistent unemployment in the absence of fiscal stimulus. In this situation, a fall in interest rates associated with an increase in the real money supply would not stimulate aggregate demand via increased investment.

The neoclassical counter-argument claims that the increase in the real money supply resulting from falling prices simply increases the real value of the public's money holdings above the desired level. This real balance or wealth effect therefore causes people to reduce savings and increase consumption thereby shifting the IS curve to the right and moving the economy back towards full employment.

The economists Clower and Leijonhufvud draw a distinction between the economics of Keynes and the Keynesian interpretation of his work. They insist that while Keynes would not necessarily dispute the existence of a wealth effect, he was mainly concerned with short-run phenomena; the dynamic analysis of the macroeconomy in disequilibrium. This is not emphasised in the Keynesian interpretation of his work. Furthermore, since in reality disequilibrium may persist owing to lack of market information and uncertainty, the neoclassical wealth effect is unlikely to occur in the politically relevant short-run.

Monetarists and Keynesians: monetarism in the 1980s

Monetarism can perhaps be viewed as a more realistic version of neo-classical theory. Monetarists believe that the major thrust of money supply changes is ultimately on prices. Such a belief is based on the argument that the public's demand for money behaviour is essentially stable and predictable, and that the economy tends towards the 'natural rate of unemployment' in the absence of government intervention. In contrast, Keynesians held that, owing to the potentially de-stabilising influence of the public's speculative demand for money, there is no reliable relationship between money supply growth and changes in money national income or prices.

The UK 'monetarist experiment' in the 1980s points to:

(1) the difficulty of achieving close control over the money supply;

(2) the problem of settling on any single policy relevant money supply definition for targeting purposes;

(3) the failure of inflation to relate at all closely to the growth of £M3, an officially targeted money supply definition up until the financial year 1987/88.

EXERCISES

Exercise 1
Mix and match

A. Comparative static equilibrium

B. LM curve

1. A wealth-induced increase in spending by the public.

2. Snapshots of the economy in different settled states with no analysis of adjustment paths in moving from one state to another following some initial change in demand or monetary conditions.

3. A reduction in private sector spending prompted by a rise in interest rates which occurs as a direct result of an increase in government spending financed from non-bank sources.

C. General equilibrium

D. Aggregate demand curve

E. Real balance effect

F. Crowding out

G. Price and wage inflexibility

H. IS-LM analysis

4. Shows all the combinations of the rate of interest and the level of national income at which the monetary sector of the economy is in equilibrium.

5. A resistance to natural market forces in both the goods and labour markets.

6. Shows all the combinations of the price level and real income at which both the real and monetary sectors of the economy are in equilibrium.

7. Examination of the impact on the national economy of changes in aggregate demand and/or the money supply in the context of a general Keynesian model.

8. The particular combination of interest and income at which both the real and monetary sectors exhibit no excess demand or supply.

Exercise 2

Practical exercise

IS-LM macroeconomic model of an economy

(All expenditure and money terms are measured in £b.)

1. $C = 5 + 0.8Yd$ Consumption

2. $Yd = Y - T$ Disposable income

3. $T = -5 + 0.25Y$ Taxes

4. $G = 82.5$ Government spending

5. $I = 40 - 1.5i$ Investment

6. $X = 35$ Exports

7. $M = 2 + 0.10Y$ Imports

8. $Y = C + I + G + X - M$ National income identity

        Goods market

9. $M^S = 80$ Money supply

10. $M^D = -1.35 + 0.40Y - 4i$ Demand for money

11. $M^S = M^D$ Money market equilibrium

        Money market

IS equation (goods market)

$Y = 2 (164.5) - 3i$

The coefficient 2 = Income/Expenditure multiplier for any given rate of interest = $1/((1-0.8)+0.8(0.25)+0.10) = 1/0.5 = 2$.

(164.5) = Sum of all exogenous expenditure terms in equations 1-7, less exogenous imports, less consumption impact of exogenous taxes.

i = Rate of interest (%)

LM equation (money market)

$Y = 2.5 (81.35) + 10i$

The coefficient 2.5 = Income/Money multiplier for any given rate of interest.

(81.35) = Money stock minus constant in demand for money equation.

i = Rate of interest (%)

Money and national income

(a) Over the range of interest rates 5-12 per cent, graph the IS and LM equations (rate of interest on the vertical axis and national income on the horizontal axis).

From your graph, determine the equilibrium values for the national income and the rate of interest. Verify your results algebraically.

(b) If at the existing equilibrium levels of Y and i export demand fell from £35b. to £30b., what would be the eventual impact on national income and the rate of interest?

(c) If the government increased the money supply by 10 per cent from its present level, by how much would money national income rise? What would happen to the income velocity of circulation of money?

(Assume that export demand stands at its original level of £35b. for the purpose of this question.)

Exercise 3

Short-answer questions

1. What are the main factors governing the steepness of the LM curve?

2. List the various factors which might cause the IS curve to shift to the right.

3. Under Keynesian assumptions, explain what happens to national income and the rate of interest following a decrease in the public's demand for money?

4. What is meant by the term 'real balance effect' and what is its significance?

5. Explain how 'crowding-out' might prevent an increase in government spending from boosting output and employment?

6. Following an increase in the money supply of 10 per cent, would you expect the retail price index to rise by 10 per cent? Briefly explain.

7. Why do monetarists recommend steady growth of the money supply?

8. Was Keynes a Keynesian? Briefly explain.

Exercise 4

Data response

The following questions are based on the data response table of figures given in Exercise 4, chapter 20. The table is of Selected Economic Indicators for UK 1985-1990.

(a) Which definition of the money stock is more closely associated with the money national income?

(b) What further information would you need in order to examine the association between the changes in the money stock and changes in:

Money and national income

1. the average level of prices.

2. UK output?

Be specific about the variable required and explain carefully, using a suitable example to illustrate, how the additional information should be used.

Exercise 5

Essay questions

1. 'Left to its own devices an economy will always tend towards a full employment equilibrium position.' Critically assess this neo-classical view of the macroeconomy.

2. Using IS-LM analysis compare and contrast Keynesian and monetarist views concerning the impact of the following on output, employment, prices and interest rates:

   (a) An increase in the money supply.

   (b) An increase in planned consumption.

   (c) An increase in government spending on goods and services.

3. 'Money has no impact on the real sector of the economy.' Discuss.

4. 'Fiscal measures which are not financed by changes in the money supply can only have a temporary influence on output and prices.' Discuss.

Exercise 6

Group discussion

The relationship between money, output and prices in the UK: 1971 - 1990. (Prior to the discussion, students should collect and analyse appropriate data, noting all relevant data sources. Analysis could be based on graphical evidence and possibly the application of regression and correlation using computer facilities.)

Points of interest for general discussion might include:

1. Data selection and any identified data problems.

2. Data analysis - choice of analytical techniques together with the purpose and appropriateness of their application in each case.

3. Interpretation of the results - any evidence of causation, identifiable time-lags, etc.

4. Which particular school of thought regarding the relationship in question is best supported by the data analysis?

136

Money and national income

ANSWERS

Exercise 1

Mix and match   A. 2   B. 4   C. 8   D. 6

                     E. 1   F. 3   G. 5   H. 7

Exercise 2

Practical exercise   (a) National income = £300bn.

                          Rate of interest = 9.67%

                          Algebraic verification:

                          IS equation $Y = 329 - 3i$

                          LM equation $Y = 203.3 + 10i$

                          In equilibrium IS = LM $\therefore$ can set the 2 equations

                          equal $\therefore$ $203.3 + 10i = 329 - 3i$

                          $$13i = 125.7$$

                          $$\therefore i = 9.67\%$$

                          You can substitute this value back into either the IS or LM equation
                          to give an equilibrium value of $Y = £300bn$

                      (b) A graphical estimate, or solution to the following simultaneous
                          equations, in which the constant term in the IS equation has been
                          adjusted by the exogenous fall in export demand X income-expenditure
                          multiplier, i.e. -5 X 2 = £-10bn

                          $$IS \quad Y = 319 - 3i$$

                          $$LM \quad Y = 203.3 + 10i$$

                          New equilibrium solution: $Y = £292.3bn.$ $i = 8.9\%$

                      (c) Money supply increase = £8bn. $\therefore$ new LM equation becomes
                          LM: $Y = 223.3 + 10i$. Setting this equation equal to the original IS
                          equation gives the following equilibrium values for Y and i:

                          $Y = £304.6bn.$ $i = 8.13\%$

                          The income velocity of circulation Y/M falls from 3.75 to 3.461.

Exercise 4

Data response   (a) On the basis of the evidence in the table below, we have the
                         following annual percentage growth patterns:

	MO	£M3	GDP
1985/6	4.2	14.6	7.3
1986/7	4.7	16.8	10.8
1987/8	7.1	18.0	11.2
1988/9	5.4	17.7	8.5

There appears to be a closer association between GDP and M4
movements but the time period is short and money supply increases
have an influence on prices after a variable time-lag which might, on
occasions, be longer than 2 years.

137

Money and national income

(b) Either information on GDP at constant prices or information on the GDP price index. Assume the former information is directly available.

Example:- based on years 85/6 and 86/7

		1985 6	1986/7	%
(1)	MO	14.2	14.8	4.2
(2)	GDP at current prices	362	388.4	
(3)	GDP at 1988/5 prices	362	367	1.38
(4)	GDP prices	100.0	105.83	5.83

The GDP price index is obtained by dividing line (2) by line (3) and multiplying the result by 100.

The percentage price change can then be compared with the percentage change in MO for the years of interest. A direct comparison can be made between output growth, as measured by GDP at 1985/6 prices, and money supply growth as measured by MO.

Exercise 5

Essay questions   1.

* Briefly explain the view emphasising the assumptions required to support it.

* Outline the Keynesian attack on this view and point out that severe depressions have occurred in many countries.

* Outline the monetarist view, emphasising the importance of market expectations and the speed at which they adjust following changes in economic circumstances.

* In practice, despite the fact that many countries have experienced high unemployment, governments are not prepared to simply rely on market forces. Demand-management policies are thought to be of positive value but there remains at least the possibility that truly left to its own devices an economy may tend to a full employment equilibrium position.

23 Cyclical fluctuations

During the post-war period the implementation of *demand management policies* led to a belief that the boom slump cycle of the nineteenth century could be controlled and that full employment could be maintained indefinitely. The return of mass unemployment and deep recession in the late 1970s has revived much interest in trade cycle theories. At least three cycles are believed to exist, the *8-10 year trade cycle*, the *50-60 year Kondratiev cycle* and a *political business cycle* of 5 years' duration.

What activates these cycles

The driving forces behind the trade cycle are a combination of the multiplier, the accelerator and business expectations. Relatively small changes in expenditure can be magnified by the effects of these three forces to cause much higher than proportionate growth in national income. Turning points at the top and bottom of the cycle are reached as built-in stabilisers exert a counter-cyclical effect on aggregate demand. For example, as income falls during a recession the tax revenues to the authorities fall and the demands on public expenditure rise so an increase in injections and a reduction of withdrawals slows the decline in national income. This also works during the boom phase of the cycle as fiscal drag causes tax revenue to rise as money incomes rise and public expenditure falls as the burden on welfare services diminishes.

The Kondratiev cycles are thought to be caused by major scientific and technological advances. Major innovations were clustered around 1790, 1825, 1885 and 1935 with the developments of steam power, railways, electric power and the motor car. All of these had profound structural effects on the economy by creating new industries and changing lifestyles. Some would say that the next Kondratiev upswing was activated by developments in microelectronics.

The political business cycle is activated by the democratic process which encourages governments to implement less politically popular policies early in office and to create more favourable economic conditions during the pre-election period.

Exercise 1

Mix and match

1. Fluctuations in real output become smaller in intensity over time.

2. Changes in expenditure which are unrelated to changes in national income.

A. Kondratiev cycle

B. Trade cycle

3. Alternating periods of expansion and contraction in business activitiy over a period of 8-10 years.

C. Explosive cycle

D. Dampened cycle

E. Exogenous change in expenditure

F. Endogenous change in expenditure

G. Cumulative movements

H. Built-in stabilisers

4. Counter-cyclical forces which cause the trade cycle to reach the upper and lower turning points.

5. Fluctuations in real output which increase in intensity over time.

6. Fluctuations in economic activity over a 50-60 year cycle caused by major technological development.

7. Changes in expenditure which are directly related to changes in national income.

8. The tendency for periods of expansion and contraction to increase in momentum.

Exercise 2

Short-answer questions

1. Explain how exports and imports act as built-in stabilisers.

2. Why do attempts at 'fine tuning' the economy through demand management often have a destabilising rather than a stabilising effect?

3. What is the role of business expectations in the theory of the trade cycle?

4. What factors explain why the trade cycle eventually reaches a lower turning point?

5. Why is it important for government and business to forecast future economic activity?

6. What do you understand by the term political business cycle?

Exercise 3

Data response

Will it be Keynes or Kondratiev? (extract from an article by Christopher Freeman in *The Guardian*, 31 August 1983)

The depression of the 1980s cannot be treated like the ordinary business cycle troughs of the 1950s and 1960s. It has structural features which have led to a high level of unemployment and which cannot be tackled by conventional Keynesian remedies, nor by waiting for a spontaneous recovery of investment. What are needed are not pre-Keynesian remedies but post-Keynesian policies. Such post-Keynesian policies must take account of the long-term implications of new technological systems. The institutional framework and the patterns of investment which brought good results in the post-war boom are no longer appropriate for the changed conditions of the 1980s and 1990s. The theories of Schumpeter and Kondratiev have something to teach us here.

Great controversy still surrounds these cycles (Kondratiev cycles) or, as many people prefer to call them 'long waves' in economic development.

Cyclical fluctuations

Many economists doubt their very existence. Such long-term fluctuations cannot be explained simply in terms of conventional business cycles theory but require an additional dimension of analysis. This involves the rise of new technologies, the rise and decline of entire industries, major infrastructural investments, changes in international location of industries and technological leadership.

The development of a viable strategy to cope with the scale of the unemployment problem of the 1980s requires a combination of the insights of Keynes with those of Schumpeter and Kondratiev. For Schumpeter, the long waves in economic life were a succession of technological transformations of the economic system. These necessitated deep structural change - a process he called 'creative destruction'.

The complexity of advanced industrial economies, the scale of public expenditure and public investment, the long time-scale of much of the research, development infrastructural investment, and the irrelevance of the unaided market mechanism in many areas, are among the reasons why a return to eighteenth- and nineteenth-century prescriptions is a delusion which would tend to perpetuate large-scale unemployment, especially in Britain.

(a) Why are Keynesian policies thought to be inappropriate to cure the depression of the 1980s?

(b) Why do some economists doubt the existence of 'long waves' of economic activity?

(c) What did Schumpeter mean by the expression 'creative destruction'?

(d) Why is the unaided market mechanism thought to be irrelevant to the present unemployment problem?

(e) Can the technological innovations of electronics in the 1980s be of the same significance to the 'long waves' as the internal combustion engine or the railways?

(f) What kind of policy measures do you think the author means by 'post-Keynesian remedies'?

Exercise 4

Essay questions

1. 'Policy measures necessary to secure full employment will lead to dis-equilibrium on the balance of payments.' Explain why this is so and how it might be avoided.

2. 'The frequent re-occurrence of economic crisis and depressions is evidence that the automatic functions of our business system are defective.' Discuss.

3. Governments nowadays are committed to a formidable range of economic objectives. To what extent do these conflict with each other?

Cyclical fluctuations

4. 'The trade cycle is purely a monetary phenomenon.' Discuss.

5. 'The government itself is frequently the cause of business
   fluctuations.' Discuss.

Exercise 6

Group discussion

It is often suggested that a political business cycle exists in that
governments may cause fluctuations in economic activity as a means of
gaining political advantage. Policy measures which are likely to be
politically unpopular but necessary for the control of the economy may be
implemented in the early stages of the life of Parliament. Governments
may seek to create more favourable economic conditions during the
pre-election period.

1. Is it really in the power of a government to change the economic
   conditions for political reasons?

2. If so, what are the means by which this could be achieved?

3. Which economic variables are likely to have the most significant
   effect on an election outcome?

4. Is the political business cycle a necessary price to be paid for
   democracy?

5. Would an authoritarian system of government be better from an
   economic standpoint?

ANSWERS

Exercise 1

Mix and match
A. 6   B. 3   C. 5   D. 1
E. 2   F. 7   G. 8   H. 4

Exercise 3

Data response

(a) Unemployment is not simply a matter of demand deficiency but involves
    major structural changes due to new technology, major changes in the
    structure of the working population and significant regional
    disparities. In addition, traditional Keynesian remedies may have
    serious implications for inflation and balance of payments.

(b) Insufficient historic data. Reliable public records of national
    income and employment only go back as far as the 1850s. This would
    only give three 'long waves', which is statistically inadequate to
    verify the theory.

(c) Major technological breakthroughs are usually responsible for
    deep-rooted structural shifts in industry. This is likely to result
    in serious short-term problems associated with immobility of factors

of production, e.g. the mass production of motor vehicles led to a
fall in employment of horse-driven coach drivers and a drop in demand
for coaches.

(d)

* Unlikely wage rates will fall in areas of high unemployment.
* Unlikely that people will 'price themselves back into employment'
  with new technological development.
* Difficult to re-establish international competitiveness on wages with
  high-valued pound due to North Sea oil.

(e)

* Microelectronics have caused major changes in industry and
  employment.
* Forecasts indicate changes in the nature of work, e.g. more home
  working.
* Substantial improvements in communications.
* New skills, training, management attitudes and business systems.

Critics would argue that it is not possible to identify 'long wave'
turning points until long after they have happened.

(f)

* Major changes in providing firms with long-term venture capital to
  finance new technological development.
* Radical new approaches to education and training to increase
  occupational mobility.
* Greater flexibility in workforce by government policy to ease the
  problems of geographic mobility of labour.
* More encouragement to unions to eliminate outdated work practices.
* Examination of the patterns of work, e.g. working week, retirement,
  school-leaving age etc.

Exercise 4

Essay questions

1.

* Increase in public spending to stimulate aggregate demand will tend
  to increase imports due to a relatively high marginal propensity to
  import for the UK.
* Relaxation of monetary controls to encourage consumer spending would
  tend to be inflationary and thus reduce export competitiveness.
* Inflationary expectations may lead to an outflow of capital as
  investors may fear a loss of real value in UK securities.

To avoid these problems, the government need to use:

* Tariffs and other trade restrictions on imports.
* Incomes policies to control wage inflation.
* Exchange controls on capital movements.
* Control of the value of the currency on foreign exchange markets.

24 Economic growth and development

It is an outstanding feature of Western economies that they have grown and prospered at a rapid rate in the past 200 years. The benefits of industrialisation have been obvious, but they have not been spread evenly. Some countries seem to be able to sustain higher than average increases in national income over long periods of time. This growth of economies leads to *development*, in that it causes changes in the structure of economies and societies. They move from relatively simple structures to ones which are advanced and very complex. We now have a situation where there are very large differences between economies of advanced industrial nations and those of less developed countries (LDC).

The major determinants of growth

There are, of course, a large number of factors which contribute towards a country's growth performance. Three of the major ones are growth of the labour supply, growth of the capital stock, and technical progress. *A growth in the labour supply* will permit increased output in an economy if there is full employment. As a consequence, it can contribute towards increased economic welfare. The most obvious source of labour supply increase is a natural increase in total population, although within Western Europe, international migration and increased participation in the labour market by women have made a significant contribution towards growth.

An *expansion in a country's capital stock* through net investment is a second source of growth. Not only is investment a component of aggregate demand, it also provides a stock of productive resources which can be combined with labour to increase output.

Technical progress is also important, in that it can contribute towards the quality of both the capital stock and the labour supply. Technical advancement can, however, be a two-edged sword if it causes unemployment. This is a hotly contested issue, as there are those who maintain that the workforce should be more flexible to avoid technological unemployment. In any case, they maintain that without the introduction of new technology, even more jobs will be lost as a result of international competition.

Policies for growth

Economic growth has generally been regarded as a good thing by most governments in that it generates resources which can be used to attain other policy objectives such as reducing poverty and increasing living standards. There are, however, negative aspects to growth including over-rapid urbanisation and potential harm to the physical environment.

Economic growth and development

In the 1970s, industrial policy with direct help being given to firms was tried, and in the 1980s there has been a greater emphasis on the market mechanism to stimulate the economy.

Theories of growth

These theories aim to describe, explain and predict the development of economies. An example is the classical theory of development which postulates that the process will bring increased prosperity, but population growth will grind down living standards back again to subsistence levels. Other theories like Rostow's talk of the stages developing economies go through. Modern theories, however, often stress the strategies which can be employed to encourage growth.

Population and development

Economists since Malthus in 1798 have been concerned that if population grows more rapidly than the level of the output, the result would be disastrous. Despite the predictions of Malthus, the earth continues to support ever-increasing populations due to improved agricultural techniques. In the West, there are many countries where stagnating population, or even population decline, is a more serious problem. In very poor countries such as Bangladesh, where population grows more rapidly than the food resources to comfortably support it, there have been periodic disasters resulting in massive loss of life.

Trade and development

The use of overseas aid to overcome the problems of LDCs is seen as essential by many. There are those, however, who assert that aid breeds dependence, and in any case it is often spent on military items which do little for the prevention of poverty. The availability of overseas markets to sell goods in and the transfer of technology via trade links is frequently regarded as a better way to promote development. Unfortunately, many advanced economies have sought to restrict imports of manufactures from LDCs, and large multi-national companies have preferred not to invest in the kinds of projects which encourage development.

EXERCISES

Exercise 1

Mix and match

1. The rate of economic growth at which planned investment is equal to planned saving. It is a requirement to stable growth.

2. The rate of growth of aggregate demand which is equal to the growth of the labour force plus the growth in labour productivity.

A. Optimum population

B. Indicative planning

C. Stationary state

D. Warranted rate of growth

E. Underdeveloped country

F. Steady state growth path

G. Natural rate growth

H. Economic growth

I. Positive checks on population growth

J. Subsistence wages

3. A method of promoting growth in an economy by setting voluntary targets for the private sector and co-ordinating government spending.

4. Where all the variables in the economy grow at a constant rate, thus keeping in the same proportions with one another.

5. A country whose level of economic development is not yet sufficiently advanced to generate the level of saving necessary to finance the investment required to further industrialisation.

6. The size of population at which a country's income per head is maximised.

7. The checks on population which increase death rates.

8. The point where economic development comes to an end.

9. The wage level where the labour force stays constant. In the Malthusian system it is the long-run equilibrium wage.

10. An increase in a country's productive capacity, identified by a sustained rise in real national income.

Exercise 2

Practical exercise

An economy in crisis. From time to time, violent movements in the price of commodities traded in the world economy, or natural disasters can affect a particular economy badly. This can lead to major crisis for underdeveloped nations which also have longer-term problems such as population pressures and low living standards. This exercise requires you to investigate the problems of a particular economy and prepare a report on its current problems. Use text books as a starting point for the project and supplement them with any material you can find in newspapers and journals. An example of an economy you might care to investigate would be that of Egypt. In this case you would include headings such as the effects of changes in oil prices, rapid urbanisation and population growth.

Exercise 3

Short-answer questions

1. What is the link between economic growth and economic development?

2. What are the main drawbacks with the Harrod-Domar model of economic growth?

3. Why is excessive population growth a burden on less developed countries?

4. Why is the participation rate of the population an important issue?

146

Economic growth and development

5. Why does the workforce frequently fear the introduction of new
    technology?

6. What are the major factors which have contributed towards the decline
    in export earnings of the less developed countries?

Exercise 4

Data response

Fig. 24.1   Population by age group (1985)

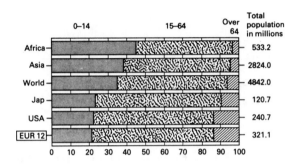

Source: Eurostat 12, 1986

What does the chart in Fig. 24.1 reveal about the population problems of:

(a) the underdeveloped world;

(b) the developed world?

Exercise 5

Essay questions

1. Discuss the view that population growth should not be of concern
    because each new consumer is also a producer.

2. Critically analyse the reasons why economic growth is sometimes
    considered harmful despite the benefits which most governments think
    it confers on society.

3. Consider the case for and against the granting of massive economic
    aid to less developed countries in order to narrow the gap in their
    development with that of the West.

4. 'Fewness of people is real poverty' (Sir William Petty). Discuss.

5. Consider the contributions that technical progress can make towards
    the process of economic growth.

6. Consider the reasons for the failure of state planning in the
    economies of Eastern Europe to give a satisfactory rate of economic
    growth.

Exercise 6

Group discussion

Development strategies. There are a number of development strategies
which less developed countries can adopt. Take a typical country in this

Economic growth and development

group like Bangladesh and debate the merits of development strategies which emphasises the following:

(a) Internally generated development, without significant contact with the world economy.

(b) A liberal trade policy.

(c) A significant donation of aid from more advanced nations.

(d) Encouraging the establishment of foreign multi-nationals.

ANSWERS

Exercise 1

Mix and match

A. 6	B. 3	C. 8	D. 1	E. 5
F. 4	G. 2	H. 10	I. 7	J. 9

Exercise 4

Data response

Fig. 24.1 reveals that there is a significant difference between the population structures of the developed world and the rest of the world.

(a) On the continents of Africa and Asia, the population of people under the age of 14 is indicative of rapid population growth and that must be a considerable burden. It should be noted, however, that not all African and Asian countries are poor and have a population problem.

(b) For the developed countries of the West, the chart shows a much smaller percentage of young people. This could be the source of the problems if population acutally falls.

Exercise 5

Essay question

1.

* This question invites the reader to accept that population growth may not be of concern.

* The growing population will eventually provide a useful supply of flexible labour.

* It also helps to generate demand for goods and services in an economy.

* For many third world countries, however, rapid population growth means that an economy has to work even harder to maintain existing living standards.

* Given the present high levels of unemployment, is it that we may have too many workers anyway?

25 Macroeconomic policies

The major *macroeconomic policy objectives* of governments are:

    (1) a high level of employment,

    (2) stable prices,

    (3) a good and sustainable rate of economic growth,

    (4) external balance,

    (5) an equitable distribution of income and wealth.

Targets set in relation to objectives are referred to as *policy targets* (e.g. 3 per cent inflation) and in order to help achieve these a variety of *policy instruments* are employed. Such instruments include *fiscal measures* (e.g. planned changes in government spending) and *monetary measures* (e.g. open market operations which influence the size of the monetary base and the level of interest rates). To achieve all policy targets simultaneously is a very difficult matter requiring both a reasonable medium-term assessment of economic developments and the correct balance and timing of policy measures; a combination which few governments manage to achieve for long.

Fiscal and monetary policies

Fiscal policy can be defined as the government's attempt to influence aggregate demand via public expenditure and tax measures whereas monetary policy can be defined as the government's attempt to influence aggregate demand by regulating the cost and availability of credit.

As IS-LM analysis clearly shows, the effectiveness of fiscal and monetary policies depends on the interest elasticity of both investment and the demand for money as well as the stability of the relevant spending and money functions. In practice, it has proved difficult to determine, with any confidence, the values of the elasticities; empirical evidence is inconclusive. Monetarists emphasise the importance of monetary rather than fiscal measures since they believe that the demand for money is interest-inelastic and consequently the LM curve rather steep. In contrast, Keynesians emphasise the importance of fiscal measures for aggregate demand management since they believe that investment is relatively interest-inelastic whereas the demand for money is interest-elastic, i.e. a relatively steep IS curve and a relatively flat LM curve.

Prices and incomes policy

Without some attempt to control prices, lasting incomes restraint would certainly be difficult to achieve. Certainly any attempt to restrict wage and salary increases in the interests of reducing wage inflation ought to be accompanied by appropriately tight fiscal and monetary measures. The Labour government did, in fact, attack inflation on all fronts in 1976 with public expenditure cuts and money supply control measures supporting their incomes policy. Such a combination of policy measures suggests a multi-causal view of inflation.

It could perhaps be argued that incomes policy is best suited to dealing with cost-push inflation. However, a case can be made for incomes policy where inflation is primarily caused by excess demand: by helping to reduce inflation expectations, income restraints can considerably ease the unemployment consequences of deflationary fiscal and monetary policies.

Problems with prices and incomes policies include misallocation of resources, since the price mechanism no longer operates to appropriately signal market forces, and the creation of a pent-up wage demand which will be released once the policy in question is terminated. The existence of strong and militant trade unions is another factor which has limited the success of incomes policy in the UK causing most policies to ultimately break down.

Regional policy   Government measures, such as grants and tax allowances, can help to reduce economic disparities between the various regions of a country and help to reduce overall unemployment and boost national income. 'Taking work to the workers' has been the main concern of UK regional policy although measures could be taken to increase labour mobility from the regions.

In measures introduced in 1984, the intention was to tie regional aid more closely to job creation. The aid has taken the form of both capital and job grants for development areas, such as Merseyside. Project grants and training grants represent forms of selective regional assistance, available for enterprises in both development areas and intermediate areas. A major objective of the 1984 reforms to regional policy was to reduce the cost per job created.

Since 1975 the UK has benefited from the EEC Regional Development Fund (ERDF) and after Italy has been the largest recipient of ERDF aid. Between 1975 and 1985 the UK received more than £1.4bn. in grants from the ERDF.

EXERCISES

Exercise 1

Mix and match

A. Policy targets

1. Exogenous variables, manipulated by the government to help achieve their policy objectives.

2. Government spending and tax measures designed to control aggregate demand.

3. A suitable measure to help combat cost-push inflation.

B. Policy instruments

4. Balance of payments equilibrium.

C. External balance

5. A form of regional assistance available to enterprises in all sectors of industry, in both development and intermediate areas.

D. Fiscal policy

E. Monetary policy

6. The values which a government attaches to its various policy objectives.

F. Incomes policy

G. Price codes

7. In operation from 1972-1979, they defined the permitted price increases with references to increases in allowable costs and to profit margins.

H. Project grants

8. The government's attempt to control aggregate demand by taking measures designed to have a direct influence on the cost and availability of credit.

Exercise 2

Practical exercise

Aggregate demand management. Macroeconomic models such as the one employed by the Treasury can be highly complex, consisting of hundreds of equations to explain the workings of the economy. Besides their use for economic forecasting purposes, such models are very useful for assessing the relative merits of alternative economic policy packages designed to meet stated policy targets for inflation, growth, employment and the balance of payments. In the context of complex models, high-powered computers are essential for this purpose.

It is possible to show the fundamental nature of aggregate demand management within the context of a simplified macroeconomic model. By forming what is called a 'reduced-form' equation for national income (national income expressed only in terms of the exogenous variables in the model) it is possible to assess the likely impact of fiscal and monetary measures on the level of aggregate demand. So, for the purpose of aggregate demand management and the attainment of stated policy targets, the strength of any required fiscal and monetary measures can clearly be determined by reference to the relevant 'reduced-form' equation.

The following equation relates the national income to exogenous expenditure and money terms and has been derived from the IS-LM model outlined in exercise 2, Chapter 22 (Money and national income). For convenience, the policy instruments have been isolated from the other exogenous terms in the equation, with the latter absorbed into the constant term. In fact, 'constant' is a misnomer in this context since exogenous consumption, investment, exports etc. can all change from one period to another to influence the level of national income.

Macroeconomic policies

$$Y = 120.78 + \underbrace{\frac{80}{1.73333}}_{\substack{\text{Monetary policy instrument} \\ \text{and associated multiplier}}} + \underbrace{\frac{82.5 - (0.8 \times -5)}{0.65}}_{\substack{\text{Fiscal policy instruments} \\ \text{and associated multiplier}}}$$

The above equation gives an equilibrium value for the national income equal to £300bn. which is fully consistent with the value determined in question (a), exercise 2, Chapter 22 (Money and national income). Before answering the following questions, refer back to that exercise and the IS-LM model on which it is based.

(a) The target level of national income for the next policy period is £330bn. It is expected that exogenous changes in investment and export demand will in the absence of any changes in monetary or fiscal policies cause national income to rise to an anticipated level of £320bn. Consequently, policy measures are required to boost national income by a further £10bn.

   You are required to examine the alternative policy measures that could be taken to hit the £330bn. target and to assess which of these is most effective on a pound for pound basis.

(b) What are the values of the relevant policy multipliers relating changes in the national income to changes in the values of policy instrument variables in the following cases:

   i) An increase in government spending financed by bond sales.

   ii) A reduction in taxes via the raising of tax thresholds.

   iii) An equal increase in government spending and taxes.

   iv) An increase in the money supply.

   v) An increase in government spending financed by an increase in the money supply.

Exercise 3
Short-answer questions

1. What are the main macroeconomic policy objectives of most governments?

2. What are policy instruments and policy targets? Give some examples of each.

3. Name two instruments of monetary policy which have been employed by the UK government and briefly explain how they might be used to influence the level of aggregate demand.

4. With the aid of an IS-LM diagram, briefly contrast the views of monetarists and Keynesians regarding the likely short-run impact of a bond-financed increase in government spending on both national income and the rate of interest.

Macroeconomic policies

5. Under what circumstances might both the IS and LM curves shift to the right as a direct consequence of an increase in government spending designed to stimulate aggregate demand?

6. What are the main problems associated with incomes policies?

7. What have been the main forms of regional aid made available to UK development areas in recent years?

8. What is meant by the term 'regional multiplier' and how does it relate to regional aid?

9. What changes have occurred in the levels and pattern of unemployment, by UK region, since 1979?

Exercise 4

Data response

With reference to Table 25.1, on the following page, answer the following questions.

(a) Which of the variables shown in Table 25.1 most closely relate to the four major macro-economic policy objectives?

(b) If the Chancellor held the sterling exchange rate to £1 = 3DM upon entry into the EMS how would this affect the UK economy?

(c) Present economic policy includes measures to increase the level of savings. What is the economic reasoning behind this?

(d) What factors account for the forecasted decline in real personal disposable incomes?

(e) What would the consequences of continued decline in stockbuilding and fixed interest?

(f) From the 1982 - 6 average figures discuss whether the state of the UK economy forecasted for 1991 is an improvement.

Exercise 5

Essay questions

1. The Phillips' curve shows that lower inflation is associated with higher unemployment. Why, then, have UK governments placed top macroeconomic policy priority, since 1975, on reducing and stabilising inflation at a low level?

2. What policy instruments has the UK government employed to help achieve its macroeconomic policy objectives in the 1980s and how far has the government been successful in terms of realising its policy targets?

3. 'If the UK government had employed Keynesian rather than monetarist policies since 1980 then employment, investment and economic growth would all be higher than they are today.' Discuss.

4. With the aid of IS-LM analysis, discuss the various factors that critically determine the effectiveness of both monetary and fiscal policy.

Table 25.1

UK FORECASTS YEAR AVERAGE	1982-74 Average	1987 Outturn	1988 Outturn	1989 Outturn	1990 Forecast	1991 Forecast
% Change Over Previous Year:						
GDP (Output measure)	3.0	4.8	4.6	2.6	1.6	2.3
Non-Oil GDP	2.7	5.2	5.4	3.7	1.4	2.3
GDP (Expenditure measure)	2.7	4.5	4.2	2.0	1.6	2.3
Domestic Demand	3.3.	5.5	7.6	3.1	0.4	1.7
Consumers' Expenditure	3.3	5.9	7.0	3.8	2.2	1.6
Government Consumption	1.1	1.0	0.4	0.9	0.7	1.0
Fixed Investment:	5.0	8.7	13.7	4.4	0.5	1.5
Manufacturing	4.5	5.1	11.7	6.3	-1.0	3.0
Dwellings	4.7	7.3	7.6	-5.1	-12.00	2.0
Stockbuilding						
(£ billion at 1985 prices)	0.5	1.2	4.3	3.1	-2.1	-1.3
Export Volume:						
Total Goods & Services	3.9	5.1	0.7	4.2	8.4	5.7
Goods Other than Oil	3.7	6.9	3.5	11.0	9.8	7.1
Import Volume:						
Total Goods & Services	6.1	7.6	12.6	7.1	3.1	3.5
Goods Other than Oil	7.7	8.2	14.5	7.9	3.4	3.7
Industrial Production	2.7	3.3	3.7	0.5	1.0	2.5
Manufacturing Production	2.2	5.3	7.3	4.3	1.5	2.5
Average Earnings*	8.0	7.8	8.7	9.1	9.6	8.7
Real Personal Disposable Income	2.3	3.2	5.3	4.8	3.4	2.5
Personal Saving Ratio	9.9	5.7	4.2	5.1	6.2	7.0
Retail Prices	5.5	4.1	4.9	7.8	9.3	6.2
Manufacturing Input Prices	3.0	3.1	3.3	5.7	0.5	2.0
Manufacturing Output Prices	5.7	3.8	4.5	5.1	6.1	5.5
Employment	0.3	2.0	3.4	3.1	1.7	-0.4
Levels:						
Unemployment (million adults)	2.88	2.82	2.29	1.80	1.63	1.85
Current Account (£ billion)	2.7	-4.4	-15.0	-19.1	-16.1	-12.2
PSBR (£ billion, financial year)	7.6	-3.4	-14.5	-7.9	-4.0	-2.0
3 Months Interback (%)	11.1	9.7	10.3	13.9	15.0	13.0
Sterling Exchange Rate Index						
(1985=100)	102.2	90.1	95.5	92.6	92.0	95.0
Dollar/Sterling	1.47	1.64	1.78	1.64	1.78	1.93
D.Mark/Sterling	3.77	2.94	3.12	3.08	2.90	2.93
END YEAR						
% Change Over Previous Year:						
Average Earnings*		8.8	10.5	7.3	9.3	8.0
Retail Prices		3.7	6.8	7.7	9.5	4.5
Manufacturing Input Prices		2.6	4.8	5.0	1.0	3.0
Manufacturing Output Prices		4.0	4.9	5.3	6.2	5.0
M0		4.2	8.5	5.7	4.5	5.0
M4		16.3	17.6	18.2	13.0	10.0
Levels:						
Unemployment (million adults)		2.57	2.04	1.63	1.70	1.95
3 Months Interbank (%)		8.9	13.1	15.1	15.0	11.0
Stering Exchange Rate Index						
(198=100)		93.6	97.4	86.0	96.0	94.0
Dollar/Sterling		1.87	1.80	1.61	1.94	1.92
D.Mark/Sterling		2.96	3.21	2.73	3.00	2.90

* Underlying rate of increase: 1987 7.8%, end year 8.5%; 1988 8.8% end year 8.75%; 1989 9.1% end year 9.25%; 1990 9.6%, end year 9.25%; 1991 8.7%, end year 8.0%

Source: *Barclays Economic Review* August 1990

Macroeconomic policies

5. In real terms the government has reduced spending on regional aid in
    the 1980s despite the considerable increase in unemployment problems
    Apart from the ability to reduce economic disparities between
    regions, are there any arguments for reversing this trend?

6. Discuss the changes in UK regional policy which have taken place
    during the 1980s. What is the government's rationale for reducing
    expenditure on regional aid in real terms?

Exercise 6

Group discussion

The class should be split into four groups. Each group should be
allocated a different economic objective i.e. Inflation, Balance of
Payments, Unemployment and Economic Growth. Each group will give a
presentation on the following:

1. To support the view that their objective should have the highest
    priority.

2. To identify the best economic indicators to measure the improvements
    in the objectives.

3. To suggest a 'package' of economic policies to improve their
    economic objective.

4. To consider whether membership of the European Monetary System would
    be likely to improve their objective (a) in the short run, (b) in
    the long run.

Other groups should be given the opportunity to ask questions which
challenge the importance of each economic objective.

ANSWERS

Exercise 1

Mix and match   A. 6   B. 1   C. 4   D. 2
                 E. 8   F. 3   G. 7   H. 5

Exercise 2

Practical exercise   (a) The most effective policy measure is an increase in government
                           spending which is financed by bank borrowing i.e. an increase in
                           government spending directly financed by an increase in the money
                           supply.
                           Required final change in Y = £10bn.
                           $\Delta G = \Delta M = \lambda$

155

Therefore, applying both the income-expenditure and income-money multipliers in the 'reduced-form' equation we have,

$$\frac{1}{1.7333} \lambda + \frac{1}{0.65} \lambda = 10$$

$$\therefore \left(\frac{1}{1.7333} + \frac{1}{0.65} \right) \lambda = 10$$

$$\therefore 2.115 \ \lambda = 10 \quad \lambda = 4.728$$

So, the required increase in government spending, to be financed by bank borrowing, is £4.728bn. This represents the smallest possible injection into the economy to achieve the national income policy target of £330bn.

(b) (i)   1.538

     (ii)   1.231

     (iii) 0.307

     (iv)   0.577

     (v)   2.115

Exercise 4

Data response

(a) GDP - would indicate the level of economic growth.

Unemployment - a low level of unemployment objective.

Retail Price Index - stable prices.

Current Account. - External trade balances.

(b) £1 = 3DM is a comparatively high exchange rate which would cause UK goods to be expensive abroad and imports into the UK would be relatively cheap. Therefore the current account deficit would worsen. This could also affect unemployment rates as industrial production declined. A high exchange rate would have positive effects on the Retail Price Index as imported supply prices would fall.

(c) A higher level of savings would reduce domestic consumption which would reduce demand pull inflation. It might also improve availablility of funds for industrial investment.

(d) Real personal disposable income would decline due to rising unemployment and inflation increasing above the level of earnings. It might also fall if taxation was increased to bring inflation under control.

(e) Over the longer term it would reduce industry's competitiveness as more outdated equipment would be in use. This would limit the economy's growth potential and external trade position.

Macroeconomic policies

(f) Serious worsening of external trading position with a decline in sterling exchange rate index as a consequence. Higher levels of interest rate and a declining industrial base due to low levels of investment. On the positive side a lower level of unemployment and a negative PSBR.

Exercise 5

Essay questions   1.

* Briefly explain the Phillips' curve.

* Note that the Phillips' curve broke down towards the end of the 1960s and that subsequently unemployment has, on occasions, been observed to rise with inflation.

* Mention some of the problems associated with inflation, noting the possible investment consequences of inflation-induced uncertainty concerning business profit expectations.

* Note that the government expected some short-term increase in unemployment to result from its anti-inflation policies, but that in the longer term stabilising inflation at a low level is expected to stimulate economic growth and reduce the level of unemployment.

* Mention some relevant inflation, growth and employment statistics.

26 Unemployment

The causes and consequences of unemployment are without doubt one of the most crucial political questions of the 1980s and are the point of intense debate between conflicting economic perspectives. This chapter seeks to help give an understanding of differing views on why unemployment occurs, what alternative policy measures are available to governments and the limitations of these measures in practice.

Measurement of
unemployment

Estimates of unemployment vary between 2 and 5 million depending on the way in which it is defined. Official figures are calculated by the number of people claiming benefit at employment offices on an appointed day of the month. This figure is often claimed to be an underestimate as many people are unemployed and yet not claiming benefit or are not entitled to it, e.g. housewives, school-leavers and students on YTS and other schemes. It must also be remembered that the 'black economy' may overstate registered unemployment as some people may be in receipt of benefit and also working.

The costs of
unemployment

Whatever figure is accepted as the real level of unemployment it must be acknowledged that unemployment imposes severe personal, social and economic costs. Personal costs would include a psychological burden on the individual of depression, alienation and lost confidence. Many surveys have shown that the non-money rewards from work are a major contribution to an individual's self-esteem and personal motivation. The social costs are often a consequence of the psychological pressure of unemployment, e.g. divorce, suicide, crime, drugs and vandalism. The economic costs to the Exchequer include the burden of unemployment on the tax payer for welfare and unemployment benefits and lost tax revenues. On a macroeconomic level, unemployment represents unused productive resources which have an opportunity cost in term of the GNP.

Causes of
unemployment

Reference has already been made in earlier chapters to the debate over the extent to which unemployment is 'voluntary' or 'involuntary'. Supply-side economists subscribe to the view that imperfections in the labour market prevent the fall in wages which would stimulate growth of output and employment. This is referred to as the *excessive real wage* hypothesis. It is argued that removal of imperfections would allow unrestricted market forces to exert a downward pressure on wages and inflation and as a result real money values would rise and thus stimulate aggregate demand. This is the so called *Pigou effect*. Growth in the

Unemployment

economy would continue to rise until equilibrium in the labour markets has been reached at the full employment level. Monetarists take the view that a level of 'natural' unemployment will always be present even if labour markets are in equilibrium due to search unemployment, seasonal factors, structural unemployment and the residual group. The Keynesian view asserts that unemployment is largely 'involuntary' as it occurs when a deflationary gap exists in the economy due to a deficiency of aggregate demand.

Policy measures

A belief in the excessive real wage hypothesis would lead to the conclusion that the role of the state is to clear the way towards a labour market free from imperfections, e.g. improved information availability, improved labour mobility, re-training, trade union legislation and removal of statutory minimum wages. Advocates of this view would also argue the importance of tax cuts to motivate people towards employment and to reward enterprise. An acceptance of the demand deficient hypothesis would lead to the conclusion that state demand management initiatives were needed to close the deflationary gap. This could be done by fiscal measures e.g. public sector spending increased or by monetary growth.

EXERCISES

Exercise 1

Mix and match

A. Search unemployment

B. Natural unemployment

C. Occupational immobility of labour

D. Residual unemployment

E. Structural unemployment

F. Geographic immobility of labour

G. Demand deficient unemployment

1. The number of persons unemployed when the labour market is in equilibrium.

2. The level of unemployment caused by long-term shifts in demand and technological change.

3. The obstacles which prevent a worker transferring from one occupation to another.

4. Short-term unemployment due to imperfect information in the labour market.

5. Obstacles which prevent a worker from taking employment in another part of the country.

6. The number of workers who are regarded as unemployable due to disability or the effects of long-term unemployment.

7. Unemployment caused by a recession in the economy which will have adverse effects in all sectors and in all regions.

Exercise 2

Practical exercise

Complete Table 26.1 by reference to *Annual Abstract of Statistics*, *Social Trends* and *The Department of Employment Gazette*.

Unemployment

Table 26.1

	1971	1976	1986	1981	1989
Home population					
Total working population					
Unemployment					
Total employed					
Employment by industry					
Agriculture, forestry and fishing					
Energy and water supply					
Extraction of minerals and ores					
Metal goods, engineering and vehicles					
Other manufacturing					
Construction					
Distribution, hotels and catering					
Transport and communications					
Banking, finance and insurance					
Other services					
All industries and services					

(a) Group the categories into primary, secondary and tertiary employment.

(b) What is the percentage of employees in primary, secondary and tertiary employment in (i) 1971, (ii) 1989?

(c) What are the percentage changes of employees in these groups between 1971 and 1989?

(d) What are the possible explanations for this trend?

(e) What is the likely impact on regional patterns of employment?

(f) To what extent is 'deindustrialisation' desirable and unavoidable?

Exercise 3
Short-answer
questions

1. What do you understand by the term 'search unemployment'? To what extent is a high level of search unemployment a sign of economic growth?

2. Critics of the YTS scheme often claim it disguises a much larger unemployment total. How can this view be supported and challenged?

3. Would protectionist measures against imports provide a long-term solution to unemployment?

4. Let $C = 500 + 0.75Yd$, $I = 750$, $T = 0.1Y$ and $G = 3000$. If the economy is closed to foreign trade and the full employment level of national

income is estimated to be 15,000, then how much additional government expenditure is required to attain this level?

5. What factors are likely to reduce geographic mobility of labour in the UK?

6. Draw a diagram to show a long-run Phillips' curve at the natural rate of unemployment. Explain it briefly.

7. What factors have caused the significant increase in female activity rates in the period since the last war?

Exercise 4

Essay questions

1. How far is it realistic to expect the problems of regional unemployment to be solved by market forces?

2. 'The current recession has awakened in some quarters a peculiar fatalism which suggests a return to full employment is impossible, even undesirable' (J. Eatwell). Discuss.

3. 'In a sense unemployment is all frictional.' How far would you agree?

4. 'The persistence of high unemployment in an expanding economy is a largely self-inflicted problem caused by the traditions of British pay bargaining' Discuss.

5. 'The rate of unemployment is 100 per cent if it is you that is unemployed.' Discuss the economic and social impact of the present high levels of unemployment.

Exercise 5

Group discussion

The discussion takes the form of a meeting of the National Economic Development Council (NEDC) which has been called to consider the strengths and weaknesses of a number of proposals to reduce unemployment. Present at the meeting are representatives of employers' organisations, government, trade unions and other interested parties. The formal motions which have been tabled for discussion are:

1. A motion from the TUC for reductions in the working week and an undertaking from employers to reduce the present high levels of overtime working in manufacturing industry.

2. A proposal from the Treasury to enact substantial tax cuts in the next Finance Act, particularly in personal income tax and corporation taxes.

3. A motion from employers calling for a wider acceptance on the part of trade unions and government of the use of part-time workers and an

end to the barriers which reduce occupational and geographic mobility of labour.

The meeting should consider the relative strengths and weaknesses of each of the motions and come to a decision on which, if any, of the proposals would be most effective.

ANSWERS

Exercise 1

Mix and match   A. 4   B. 1   C. 3   D. 6   E. 2   F. 5   G. 7

Exercise 4

Essay questions   1.

* Free market solution to unemployment would argue labour rates and other business costs would be lower in depressed areas.

* Eventually the relative differences in costs would cause profit-maximising firms to move to depressed areas.

* Equally, the higher production costs and overuse of economic resources in full employment areas would be a disincentive to location.

* Critics of free market economics would argue that the effects of the regional multiplier would depress infrastructure, worsen labour relations and ultimately cause depopulation in depressed areas.

* The most geographically mobile workers are young, skilled and educated. Population movement away from a depressed area would reduce the area's attraction to future employers.

27 Inflation

Inflation can be defined as a persistent tendency for the general price level to rise and since the mid-1970s UK governments have attached top macroeconomic policy priority to reducing and hopefully stabilising the rate of inflation at a low level. The general price level most commonly used to measure inflation in the UK is the *retail price index* which measures changes in the weighted average price of a basket of goods and services that are typically consumed by households. The annual rate of inflation is simply the percentage increase in the retail price index over a period of one year and in 1989 it was 8%.

Effects of
inflation

Concern with inflation, especially *unanticipated inflation*, amounts to more than just the redistribution effects (e.g. from weakly unionised to strongly unionised workers) and the administrative costs associated with the more frequent preparation of new price lists by firms. There are possible adverse balance of payments effects if the domestic rate of inflation is higher than that of major competitors and there is the uncertainty that firms face regarding the influence of inflation on costs and revenues. Increased uncertainty regarding anticipated profit flows from investments can inhibit aggregate investment and reduce economic growth.

Demand and
cost inflation

One view of inflation before the 1970s was that it was simply the result of *excess aggregate demand* caused, perhaps, by government over-spending or by excessive growth of the money supply. An alternative view was that *rising money wages*, secured by trade unions, or increases in other production costs (e.g. imported raw materials) put pressure on firms' profit margins causing them to mark-up prices. Whichever view one held, the Phillips' curve showed a very close inverse association between inflation and unemployment over the period 1861-1957 indicating a clear trade-off between the two. For government policy purposes, it suggested attainable combinations of inflation and unemployment and indicated the opportunity cost of lower inflation in terms of employment, and vice versa. After 1966, however, the Phillips' curve broke down and the existing theories of inflation clearly required modification and refinement.

Modern views on
inflation

One view is that inflation is caused by excess demand and sustained by expectations. The building of anticipated inflation into wage demands causes the Phillips' curve to shift so that a trade-off between inflation and unemployment may only be observed in the short run. Now the nature of the expectation formation process is an important consideration in connection with anti-inflation policy measures. According to the *adaptive expectations hypothesis*, only past rates of inflation influence economic agents' inflation expectations whereas, in contrast, the *rational expectations hypothesis* claims that all relevant current information is taken into account. With the latter hypothesis there exists only the possibility of a very short-term trade-off between inflation and unemployment, whereas with the former, trade-offs exist in the short run, at least, owing to the lags in expectation formation.

Another view is that inflation is essentially caused by the *activities of trade unions*. It must, however, be demonstrated that trade unions became more militant during the 1960s in order to account for the sudden breakdown of the Phillips' curve and attempts to show that there was a significant increase in militancy have not been especially convincing. In any event, unless the government is unable to achieve adequate control of the money supply, it is difficult to see how such cost pressures could be a direct cause of inflation.

Alternative measures to combat inflation

Policy measures employed must reflect the underlying causes of inflation so that if it is believed to be caused by both cost and demand factors, then a combination of policy measures including fiscal and monetary restraint, and possibly an incomes policy, should be employed. If inflation is believed to be caused primarily by excess demand, then fiscal and monetary policies are appropriate with monetarists placing special emphasis on money supply control. A prices and incomes policy is appropriate in cases where inflation is believed to be primarily caused by trade union activities.

While *indexation* - e.g. tax thresholds and pensions increased in line with the RPI - tends to institutionalise inflation and does little to combat it in any direct sense, it does help remove some of the unfortunate redistributive effects that would otherwise occur.

EXERCISES

Exercise 1

Mix and match

1. The linking of economic variables - e.g. interest payments - to the rate of inflation.

2. A statistical association between unemployment and wage inflation which broke down in the late 1960s.

Inflation

3. A sustained rise in the general level of prices
   prompted by increases in money wages or raw
   material and energy prices.

A. Cost-push inflation

B. Demand-pull inflation

4. The failure of people to accurately assess the
   impact on their real incomes when money incomes
   and prices rise.

C. Indexation

5. Anticipation of the future value of a variable,
   e.g. inflation, based on observed errors between
   actual and expected values of that variable in
   the recent past.

D. Inflationary fiscal drag

E. Phillips' curve

F. Natural rate of unemployment

6. The level of unemployment established by market
   forces and towards which the economy will tend to
   return following any market disturbances.

G. Money illusion

7. A sustained rise in the general level of
   prices caused by excessive increases in
   government spending, investment or consumption.

H. Adaptive expectations

I. Rational expectations

8. A tendency for government tax receipts to
   increase as a proportion of national income owing
   to the fact that tax thresholds have not been
   raised in line with the general level of prices.

9. Anticipation based on all available and relevant
   information.

Exercise 2

Short-answer
questions

1. Briefly explain what is meant by a weighted aggregate price index.

2. What are the main harmful effects of inflation?

3. What are the main causes of inflation?

4. What are the appropriate policy measures for combating inflation
   according to monetarists such as Friedman?

5. What are the main weaknesses of the adaptive expectations hypothesis
   concerning inflation and is the rational expectations hypothesis any
   better?

6. What policy measures should be employed by a government to combat
   inflation?

7. What budget measures are necessary in relation to direct taxation in
   order to prevent inflationary fiscal drag?

8. Would indexation on the grand scale mean that inflation could safely
   be ignored? Briefly explain your answer.

Exercise 3

Data response

(a) Using the information contained in Table 27.1, determine the rate of
    inflation over the 5-year period, 1985-1989.

(b) What has happened to real personal savings over the period?

(c) In terms of demand-pull inflation, what policy view should be taken

165

Inflation

concerning the change in the average propensity to consume (APC) over the period?

Table 27.1 Consumer expenditure and personal disposable income (£bn.)

	1985	1987	1989
Consumer expenditure at current prices	217.07	264.00	324.48
Consumer expenditure at 1985 prices	217.02	242.96	269.82
Personal disposable income at current prices	239.71	280.09	341.83
Personal disposable income at 1985 prices	239.79	257.77	284.26

Source: *Monthly Digest of Statistics*, June 1986

Exercise 4

Essay questions

1. (a) Describe, in detail, how the retail price index is constructed and used to measure inflation.

   (b) What are the main failings of the retail price index as a measure of inflation?

2. 'The only true cause of inflation is excessive growth of the money supply.' Discuss this monetarist line on inflation and briefly examine the policy implications associated with the view.

3. What policy measures have UK governments employed in the fight against inflation over the last 12 years and how far have the various measures been successful?

4. 'Undue concern over inflation is unwarranted as there are few harmful effects associated with it.' Critically analyse this view in relation to UK inflation experience.

Exercise 5

Group discussion

Inflation expectations. As inflation, regardless of the initial cause, can be sustained by the public's expectations, it is important for any government in implementing anti-inflation policy measures to attempt to change these expectations relatively quickly and decisively. If they are successful, then inflation can be reduced quickly and at relatively low cost in terms of employment and output. It is therefore important that in taking policy action, governments should pay attention to the various factors, and especially their relative importance, that can influence inflation expectation formation.

1. How can we determine the expectation formation process in practice?

   (a) Are the existing theories of any use?

   (b) Does the expectation formation process become more sophisticated with experience of inflation?

Inflation

   (c) What information do employers and trade unions take into account
       in their wage negotiations?

2. How important is the uncertainty factor and do political
   considerations mean that government policy measures, however firmly
   announced, simply lack credibility because of the public's fear of
   U-turns in the run-in to general elections?

3. What factors would you take into account in assessing future
   inflation rates and why?

ANSWERS

Exercise 1

Mix and match

A. 3   B. 7   C. 1   D. 8   E. 2
F. 6   G. 4   H. 5   I. 9

Exercise 3

Data response

(a) Divide consumer spending at current prices by consumer spending at
    1980 prices and multiply the result by 100 in order to obtain the
    consumer price index (1985 = 100).

         consumer price indices for 1987 and 1989 are:

1987	1989
108.6	120.2

    Rate of inflation over the 4-year period is given by taking the
    percentage change in the value of the consumer price
    index = 20.2 per cent.

(b) In simple money terms, personal savings are given by subtracting
    consumer spending at current prices from personal disposable income
    in each year:

(£B) Savings	1985	1987	1989
	22.69	16.09	17.35

    Express these at 1985 prices. This can be done by deflating by the
    consumer price index to give:

(£B) Real savings (1985 prices)	1985	1987	1989
	22.69	14.81	14.43

         Real savings have fallen by 36%

(c) Using current price information: APC in 1985 = 0.905
                                         APC in 1987 = 0.939
                                         APC in 1989 = 0.949

    Providing there are no reduced spending pressures elsewhere in the
    economy, the government ought to take some policy measures to combat
    the increased aggregate demand consequent upon households spending,
    on average, a greater proportion of their disposable incomes. Some
    restraint in government spending or an increase in taxes might be in
    order. High interest rates will also encourage savings.

Inflation

Exercise 4

Essay questions   1.

* Focus on the family expenditure survey and expenditure weights for products, sample coverage, base period and price relatives.

* Stress that the RPI reflects a weighted average of the prices of consumer goods and services and use an example to show how the index is used to measure inflation.

* Failings of the RPI include:

(a) based on a non-random data sample;

(b) product expenditure weights may change so that the index does not *strictly* measure just price change;

(c) new products, product improvements etc. means that a change in the general level of prices is not necessarily based on the same basket of goods.

28 Balance of payments and exchange rates

The balance of payments account

The balance of payments is an accounting record of the money values of economic transactions between this and other countries over a given period. The transactions include *visible* and *invisible* trade which makes up the *current* section of the account, and *investment* flows which are included in the *capital* section of the account. Together, the current and capital sections of the account give the *total for official finance*. The account always balances in the sense that a deficit or surplus in the total currency flow is made up by official finance. This can be either adjustments to the official reserves or changes to the level of international debt. A long-term imbalance in the overall balance of payments will require some policy changes to alter the demand for exports or imports as official financing can only be used as a short-term measure. Such policies might include protectionist measures, demand management through fiscal or monetary measures or currency value realignment.

Exchange rate system

Changes in the value of the pound can usually be explained in terms of the standard demand and supply model since the foreign exchanges display many of the characteristics of a perfect market. The equilibrium price of the pound changes continually as it is determined by the flows of imports and exports, speculative demands, international rates of interest and many other factors. Long-term balance of payments problems are likely to be caused by an inappropriate rate of exchange, e.g. a deficit on balance of payments could occur if, due to currency overvaluation, exports were relatively expensive and imports were relatively cheap.

Free market economists would argue that balance of payments deficits can best be solved by a *floating exchange rate* which would allow an unrestricted currency market to automatically adjust to a lower rate of exchange. It is argued that such a system would free a government from the need for any policy changes and would avoid the potential policy clashes with other elements of overall economic strategy. However, post-war experience has shown governments to be reluctant to allow a completely 'clean float' since continual currency changes erode business confidence and the system is vulnerable to the destabilising influence of speculation. Authorities have always been faced with the dilemma that some flexibility is necessary to accommodate long-term changes in the structure of international trade and yet when adjustments are made they frequently precipitate a 'currency crisis' with major political and economic repercussions. The IMF system of adjustable pegging established in 1944 attempted a compromise by maintaining fixed parities between currencies but allowing limited unilateral adjustments within a set band and more substantial changes only by international agreement. Fundamental problems of international liquidity and a succession of currency crises led to a collapse of this system in 1971. The managed flexibility or 'dirty float' established since then allows market forces a greater freedom but authorities reserve the right to manage the exchange rate by market intervention to avoid severe currency instability. This system has led to substantial oscillations in the value of the pound, most noticeably when it reached parity with the dollar in early 1985. For this reason many have advocated a return to a fixed rate system.

 Membership of the Exchange Rate Mechanism (ERM) of the European Monetary System (EMS) would impose a more rigid exchange rate regime on Sterling as it would be required to remain within a narrowly defined exchange rate band against other European currencies. Each currency is assigned a central rate against the European Currency unit (ECU) with a 2.25% band of fluctuation allowed either way. Currency fluctuation beyond the 'divergence threshold' would trigger intervention by the European central banks with funds from the European Monetary Co-operation Fund (EMCF). It is clear that this system is intended to be the forunner of a system of complete monetary integration in the European Community involving a common currency, a Central Bank and common monetary and fiscal policies. Some concern is still being expressed about the implication for sovereignty and the growing strength of a united Germany.

EXERCISES

Exercise 1

Mix and match

A. Visible trade

B. Invisible trade

C. Exchange equalisation

D. Depreciation

E. Devaluation

F. Hedging

G. Exchange controls

1. A technique of insurance against adverse fluctuations in exchange rates by manipulation of spot and forward currency contracts.

2. The reduction in the value of a currency in terms of others under a floating exchange system.

3. The difference between the value of exports and imports of tangible goods in a given period.

4. A technique operated by the Bank of England to stabilise the value of the pound on foreign exchange markets by the sale and purchase of currencies.

5. A limit on the sale and purchase of foreign and domestic currencies imposed by the authorities.

6. The balance of payments and receipts accruing from international trade in services in a given period.

Balance of payments and exchange rates

7. The reduction in the value of a currency in terms of others under a fixed exchange system.

Exercise 2

Practical

exercise

With reference to Table 28.1 answer the following questions:

(a) Calculate the balance of trade, balance of payments on current account and the balance for official finance.

(b) Calculate an appropriate official financing section for the overall account.

(c) What conclusions can be drawn about the present international trading position of the country?

(d) What policy measures would you suggest are now required?

(e) What are the implications of such policy measures for the international value of the currency?

(f) If the country had a high level of unemployment, what policy complications can be foreseen?

Table 28.1 A country's annual international trading activities

Credits		Debits	
Visible exports	15,000	Visible imports	17,000
Travel and tourism	250	Travel and tourism	750
Banking services	575	Banking services	370
Financial services	330	Financial services	520
Transport	360	Transport	220
Interest, profits and dividends	950	Interest, profits and dividends	825
Private transfers	375	Private transfers	680
Government transfers	700	Government transfers	500
Overseas investment in government stock	2,500	Overseas investment in government stock	575
Overseas private investment	3,750	Domestic private overseas investment	1,500

Exercise 3

Short-answer

questions

1. What are the problems in using domestic deflation as a means of correcting a balance of payments deficit?

2. How can firms overcome the problems of uncertainty created by a floating exchange rate?

3. If the UK/German exchange rate was £1 = 3 DM, what is the UK price of a German camera costing 375 DM? If the DM was revalued by 20 per cent, what would be the new UK price?

4. 'The central bank again supported the value of the pound in the foreign exchange markets today.' If this statement appeared in the *Financial Times*, what would it mean? Explain with a diagram.

Balance of payments and exchange rates

5. What do you understand by the term 'international liquidity'?

6. Explain the circumstances in which the supply curve for the pound would slope downwards from left to right.

Exercise 4

Data response

With reference to Table 28.2 answer the following questions:

(a) To what extent can the figures be regarded as an improvement in the UK balance of payments during the period shown.

(b) What factors contribute to the explanation of the trend in the UK balance of trade shown in the figures?

(c) How will changes in the price of oil affect the UK balance of payments and the value of the pound in the next few years?

(d) How far can the UK balance of payments rely upon continued growth in invisible earnings?

(e) What are the implications of the figures for the future pattern of employment in the UK economy?

Table 28.2

	1980	1982	1984	1986	1988
Manufactures	5457	3391	-3879	-5492	-14830
Oil	315	4643	6937	4056	2787
Other*	-4788	-5147	-7920	-7517	-8989
Total visibles	1361	2331	-4384	-8463	-20826
Private Sector Invisibles	4350	4978	9389	11983	10362
Government invisibles	-2579	-3253	-3791	-4542	-4470
Total invisibles	1555	1704	5858	7483	5892
Current a/c balance	2961	4035	1474	-980	-14665

*Food, drink, tobacco, basic materials, non-oil fuels
Source: *UK Balance of Payments 'Pink Book'* Central Statistics Office 1989

Exercise 5

Essay questions

1. 'What the world economy needs now above all else is a return to a fixed exchange rate system.' Discuss.

2. How valid are the objections to a freely floating exchange rate?

3. A change in export earnings will lead to a more than proportionate effect on national income. Discuss.

4. 'The balance of payments will always balance and therefore it is not an economic problem.' Discuss.

5. 'It would be prudent for Britain to plan on the basis that there may be no oil surplus by 1990 and a deficit again by the end of the century.' (House of Lords report, 1985). What are the implications ᵢ this conclusion for the UK balance of payments and the value of the pound?

6. Compare and contrast tariffs and exchange rate depreciation as means of correcting a balance of payments deficit.

7. What would be the consequences of an imposition of deflationary policies on the less developed countries as a means of reducing their international debts?

Exercise 6

Group discussion

Soviet Union heads towards a fully convertible rouble

Moscow to set up currency exchanges by George Sivell

The Soviet Union took its first faltering step towards a full market economy yesterday when Tass news agency declared that foreign-exchange markets, where hard currencies could be bought and sold against the ailing rouble, would be set up from January 1 next year.

The move follows a compromise last week between the Soviet President Mikhail Gorbachev and his radical opponent Boris Yeltsin, president of the Russian republic, on establishing a market economy in the Soviet Union.

Soviet authorities now appear anxious to speed up moves towards a fully convertible rouble and a full market economy because of a deepening economic crisis in the USSR.

A central exchange will be established in Moscow with other exchanges in the capitals of the republics and major cities. Gosbank, the Soviet state bank, will control the operations of the new exchanges. But Vneshekonombank, the state bank for foreign economic relations, and various ministries in the republics, will provide support for the rouble, according to Tass.

The currency exchanges will be the first to operate in the Soviet Union since the 1920s. However, they will deal only with Soviet-registered companies, not with overseas companies and not with individuals.

Since August 1, Soviet citizens have been allowed to hold hard currency and spend it in specially re-opened hard currency stores.

Many Soviet citizens use the black market to turn their roubles into dollars, marks or pounds. They then use the hard currency to buy luxury goods which again are usually available only from black market dealers.

At the official rates of exchange, the rouble is worth one pound or $1.87. A special rate of 10 roubles to the £1 which appplies to tourist spending money, though not to hotel or transport bills. On the black market, one pound can easily fetch 15 roubles.

The difference between the official currency rates fixed by the authorities and the black market rate is certain to cause problems for the hard-pressed Soviet authorities when dealing begins in January.

Balance of payments and exchange rates

Yesterday, Tass emphasised that Gosbank and Vneshekonombank would
use Soviet government and republic funds to support the rouble.

Already this year, Soviet authorities have held two auctions for hard
currency. At both, Soviet companies bid at rates close to black market
rates for foreign currencies.

Economists fear the devastating impact that a move to a fully
convertible rouble will have on the Soviet economy. Such a move had not
been expected until close to the year 2000.

Source: *The Times* 8th August 1990

The discussion is to take place between two opposing groups of economic
advisers to the Soviet President, Mikhail Gorbachev. Group one will
support the case for immediate convertability between the rouble and
western currencies in a free market. The other group should argue that
the consequences of full convertability would be too devasting on the
Soviet economy.

Issues which should be discussed include:

1. Can the Soviet Union move towards a free market economy without full
   convertability of their currency?

2. What would be the problem of establishing a workable exchange rate
   and how could it then be maintained?

3. How would the existence of a black market distort the workings of the
   currency market?

4. Could the rouble be allowed a 'free-float' against western currencies
   or should the rate of exchange be 'fixed'?

5. Is the current official exchange rate of one rouble = one pound
   sterling likely to be realistic?

ANSWERS

Exercise 1
Mix and match   A. 3   B. 6   C. 4   D. 2   E. 7   F. 1   G. 5

Exercise 2
Practical exercise   (a) Balance of trade -2,000, Balance of payments (c/a) -2,325,
                       Total currency flow +1,850.

Balance of payments and exchange rates

(b)   -1,000 official reserves

       - 850 overseas loans
       _____

       -1,850 Total official finance
       _____

(c) Poor performance of visible and invisibles on the current account
    disguised by substantial capital inflows. High rates of interest are
    most likely to be responsibe for capital inflows.

(d) This is only one year's figures and substantial policy changes would
    be unnecessary unless these figures were part of a trend over several
    years. Short-term exchange equalisation may give way, in the longer
    term, to domestic deflationary policies and devaluation to correct
    the current account deficits.

(e) Downward pressure on the currency likely as speculators would expect
    policy measures to restore competitiveness of exported goods and
    services.

(f) Domestic deflationary policies to reduce import penetration would
    also have an adverse effect on domestic aggregate demand.

Exercise 4

Data response   (a)

* serious decline in non-oil visible trade balance;

* growth in oil balance and invisible balance has disguised this
  decline but these are now declining

* serious imbalance in essential raw materials, food and non-oil fuels;

* overall little improvement demonstrated on current account; the
  long-term implications are of weakness in manufacturing sector.

(b)

* overvalued pound due to high interest rates;

* growth of import penetration in manufacturing;

* long-term de-industrialisation;

* increase in revenues from oil sales due to higher world prices.

(c) if prices fall:

* higher balance of trade deficit due to falling revenues from oil
  sales offset to some extent by lower imported oil cost.

* weakness in the value of the pound due to speculative pressure;

* in the long term, falling oil prices may cause a world recovery in
  aggregate demand.

  if prices rise:

* stronger pound.

* higher inflationary pressure due to increased cost of petrol etc.

* possible deepening of world recession.

Balance of payments and exchange rates

(d)

* growth in world competition in service industries;
* strength in tertiary sector may depend on strength in manufacturing in longer term;
* some invisibles are not easily transferable to foreign markets.

(e)

* transfer of employment from manufacturing to tertiary sectors;
* growth in female employment in service industries (more part-time employment);
* increased unemployment due to de-industrialisation;
* regional differences in employment may emerge due to heavy localisation of manufacturing.

Exercise 5
Essay questions   1.

* fixed exchange rates create stability of trading conditions and business confidence;
* speculative trade in currencies may be unprofitable.

For

* world economic co-operation to supervise system; would stimulate growth;
* would avoid the adverse effects on inflation and unemployment of currency changes;
* market mechanism imperfect due to intervention by authorities

Note Marshall/Lerner elasticity conditions and speculation.

Against

* adjustment problems for long-term changes in pattern of trade;
* timing and magnitude of devaluations;
* international liquidity;
* willingness of authorities to put self-interest aside for international co-operation doubtful.

29 Trade policy

In 1988, exports of goods from the UK amounted to 19.7 per cent of GDP and imports to 23.2 per cent of GDP. In such a situation, a government's attitude towards trade policy is likely to be important, given its widespread implications for the domestic economy. If the simple theories of international trade were to be accepted, there would be no alternative to free trade. However, there can be few countries in the world that do not operate some kind of trade restriction.

Tariff and non-tariff barriers

The imposition of *tariffs* is the traditional instrument of protectionism, although partly as a result of the General Agreement on Tariffs and Trade (GATT) they are somewhat less important than in the past. The average tariff on industrial goods in 1988 is likely to be 4.8 per cent for the European Community (EEC), 4.4 per cent for the USA and 2.2 per cent for Japan. The growing menace has been from *non-tariff barriers*. Although many non-tariff barriers are imposed to meet requirements of the domestic economy, as in the case of health regulations, they affect the ability of imports to sell into the market. In recent years, governments have deliberately sought to use *non-tariff* barriers as a way of obstructing trade. They are a particular menace because, unlike tariffs, they cannot be simply overcome by a price reduction.

Argument for protectionism

Protectionism is frequently justified on a number of grounds despite its apparently adverse affect on economic welfare. In a micro sense, it is justified on the basis that imports have an adverse affect on domestic industry. In the case of infant industries, it is argued that new industry may find it difficult to get started while facing severe competition from foreign producers, who already have substantial technical advantages. In the case of industries facing decline, it is argued that a period of protection may be required in order to allow adjustments to take place. If protection is permanent, however, then domestic industry has no incentive at all to improve its performance.

In an era of high unemployment or slow economic growth, general protection may be advocated in order to maintain jobs or to overcome balance of payments problems caused by an attempt to expand domestic demand. The objection to this kind of policy, and indeed all protectionism, is that it may invite retaliation. If all countries indulge in protectionism, then the benefit of international trade will be lost to all.

Exercise 1

Mix and match

A. Exchange controls

B. Voluntary export restraint

C. Quota

D. Infant industry

E. Dumping

F. Strategic industry

G. Export subsidy

1. Payment made to business to encourage them to export.

2. Industries felt too important in times of crisis.

3. Limits placed upon the import or export of currency.

4. The selling of a product on overseas markets at a price lower than that which applies on the home market.

5. A newly established industry which is particularly vulnerable to competition from imports.

6. The agreed limitation of sensitive exports into a particular market.

7. A physical limit placed upon the quantity of goods traded.

Exercise 2

Short Answer
Questions

1. How might an imports deposit scheme help a country's balance of payments?

2. How might the introduction of a tariff improve the terms of trade?

3. Why is dumping regarded as a problem?

4. What is the economic case for defending infant industries?

5. Why are non-tariff barriers so difficult to overcome?

Exercise 3

Data response

Table 29.1
Summary of the consumer cost of EC anti-dumping measures affecting consumer electronics imports

	Annual EC consumer cost £ million	Annual UK consumer cost £ million
Video cassette recorders:		
1983 VER agreement	175	80
1988 anti-dumping duties	174	48
Compact disc players	97	17
Computer printers:		
dot-matrix	340	55
daisy-wheel	44	7
Video cassettes	34	7
Electronic typewriters	74	12
Photocopiers	226	46
Small screen colour televisions	6	2
Total cost	1170	274

Source: *International Trade and the Consumer, Working Paper 1 National Consumer Council, 1990, P57.*

Trade policy

(a) Explain what is meant by anti-dumping measures.

(b) Suggest why these areas have been targeted for this kind of protection.

(c) Explain why the cost of protection has been so high for the consumer.

(d) Why is the loss of welfare for the importing nation likely to be less than the welfare loss of the consumer?

Exercise 5   The GATT has a major role in ensuring that the world trading system operates efficiently and that its members do not resort to excessive protectionism. As part of this process, regular rounds of trade talks are held in order to move the process of liberalisation forward.

Divide into three groups representing the interests of the developing world, the new industrialised countries, and the developed world. Prepare to make statements about what you might expect to get from the other groups in order to gain your cooperation. Remember that there may well be disagreements between the members of your group with regard to some issues, for example, the EC and the United States do not fully agree on what should be done with regard to trade in agricultural products.

ANSWERS

Exercise 1

Mix and match   A. 3   B. 6   C. 7   D. 5
                 E. 4   F. 2   G. 1

Exercise 3

Data response   (a) Anti-dumping measures are restrictions placed upon imports into a country which are regarded as being too cheap. Note: that there has been considerable argument as to the extent to which the EC is using these measures as a form of protectionism, rather than there being a legitimate form of defence against unfair trading practices.

(b) These are areas which have been selected for protection because of the fear that there will be a total loss of the domestic market. In addition the use of these kind of measures might be an incentive for producers to establish themselves within the EC.

(c) There will be gains by the producer in the form of higher prices. Also in the longer term there may be gains due to foreign direct investment and increased domestic output.

30 The European Community

Economic integration is the growing together and increasing interdependence of economies. This has been encouraged by the formation of the European Economic Community (EEC) at the centre of which is a customs union. A *customs union* is an area of free trade surrounded by a common external tariff (CET). Although a customs union encourages trade between members of the union, this *trade creation* may be offset by *trade diversion*. The UK, for example, found that it had to import food from the more expensive EEC producers, once it became a full member of the Community. This in turn denied consumers the benefits of the cheap food available on world markets.

The EEC was formed in 1958, since when it has increased membership three times. In 1973 the UK, Denmark and Ireland joined, and in 1981 Greece joined; finally, in 1986, Spain and Portugal became members taking the EEC's total population up to 320 million. The EEC is meant to be more than a customs union, it is supposed to be a *common market*, with free movement of capital, labour and enterprise. Also, national commercial legislation should be harmonised in such a way that it does not discriminate against other Community members.

To the UK, membership has been something of a disappointment, because the hoped-for dynamic gains to the UK economy failed to materialise. Slow growth has been a problem throughout Europe since the oil crisis of 1973. The budgetary costs of membership have also been high, because the UK's agricultural sector is small and unable to take full advantage of the fact that over 60 per cent of spending goes on that one policy area. In assessing the costs and benefits of membership, it should be remembered, however, that it is difficult to say what would have happened to the UK economy if it had not been part of the EEC.

The inclusion of the East German economy into the Community will take total population to nearly 340 million. Membership of the EC for the UK was for many years something of a disappointment. This was in part due to the fact that the rate of economic growth in the 1970's and early 1980's was poor throughout Europe, and so many of the anticipated benefits failed to materialise. Also there were substantial problems for the UK related to the level of budgetary contributions. These were resolved as a result of the settlements of 1984 and 1988.

The EC is meant to be more than a customs union, it is supposed to be a *common market*, with free movement of capital, labour and enterprise. Also national commercial legislation should be harmonised in such a way that it does not discriminate against other Community members. In 1985, the launch of the campaign to complete the *Single European Market* (SEM) by the end of 1992 gave new life to the process of economic integration. It

The European Community

is expected that the rate of economic growth will increase as a result of the barriers coming down, although the extent of these benefits is unclear. The fact that Eastern Europe has now decided to move towards a more market based system of economic management, has led to the prospect of further nations joining the Community. There are also likely to be further applications for membershop from the European Free Trade Area (EFTA) countries and some Mediterranean states. This is likely to mean that the market will not be complete until at least the 2000's.

EXERCISES

Exercise 1

Mix and match

A. Trade creation

B. Variable level

C. Custom union

D. Common market

E. Free trade area

F. Common external tariff

G. Intervention price

H. Optimal sustainable yield

1. A tariff used to protect agriculture which goes up and down in response to changes in world prices in such a way that it is impossible to undercut EC domestic prices.

2. A tariff wall that is of uniform height.

3. An area of free trade *not* protected by a common external tariff where tariff revenues are *not* shared.

4. An area where there is free movement of goods and the factors of production, and where commercial legislation is harmonised.

5. The floor prices for certain agricultural prices.

6. The level of fish catches which can be sustained in the long term.

7. Increased trade as a result of the creation of a customs union.

8. An area of free trade protected by a common external tariff where tariff revenues are shared on the basis of an agreed formula.

Exercise 2

Practical exercise

The effects of forming a customs union. The following data refers to tennis balls produced in country A (quantity in thousands, time period 1 year).

Price in pence	10	15	20	25	30	35	40	45	50	55	60	65	70	75	80
Domestic demand	70	65	60	55	50	45	40	35	30	25	20	15	10	5	0
Domestic supply	0	5	10	15	20	25	30	35	40	45	50	55	60	65	70

The world supply is perfectly elastic at 15p per ball.

The supply by country B is perfectly elastic at 25p per ball.

(a) Construct a diagram on squared graph paper using the above data.

(b) What is the output in country A if there are no imports allowed?

(c) Prior to the formation of the customs union, A allows imports subject to a tariff of 20p per ball. How many tennis balls are produced domestically and how many imported?

(d) If country A and country B form a customs union, how many tennis balls are produced domestically, and how many are purchased from country B?

(e) Indicate on your diagram the welfare gains from increased consumption and in trade creation.

(f) Indicate the area by which trade diversion reduces welfare.

(g) Has the customs union resulted in an increase in welfare in country A?

Exercise 3

Short-answer questions

1. What is meant by the dynamic effects of membership of a common market?

2. Under what conditions is the formation of a customs union regarded as harmful?

3. Why has the CAP proved harmful to the interests of the UK?

4. Why is it important to control the level of fish catches in the EC?

5. Why is monetary stability important to the CAP?

Exercise 4

Data response

Table 30.1   United Kingdom contributions to and receipts from the Community Budget

	Million ecu				£ Million			
	1987	1988	1989	1990	1987	1988	1989	1990
GROSS CONTRIBUTION								
Agricultural and sugar levies	502	322	286	210	354	214	192	150
Customs duties	2,008	2,175	2,438	2,482	1,415	1,445	1,638	1,773
VAT own resources including VAT adjustments and before abatements	4,871	4,314	5,058	6,132	3,433	2,866	3,398	4,534
United Kingdom abatement of VAT	-1,636	-2,399	-1,718	-2,285	-1,153	-1,594	-1,154	-1,697
IGA contributions	0	923	0	0	0	613	0	0
Fourth Resources Payments	0	0	533	0	0	0	358	0
Total Contribution	5,746	5,334	6,596	6,539	4,049	3,544	4,431	4,760
RECEIPTS								
Receipts other than refunds	3,140	3,167	3,150	3,619	2,213	2,104	2,116	2,585
Own resources refunds	165	116	0	0	116	77	0	0
Total Receipts	3,303	3,284	3,150	3,619	2,328	2,182	2,116	2,585
NET CONTRIBUTION	2,442	2,050	3,446	2,920	1,721	1,362	2,315	2,175

Notes
1. For all years sterling figures reflect actual payments made during the year, not payments in respect of particular budgets. The corresponding ecu figures are converted from sterling at the appropriate annual average exchange rate (see annex. paragraph 6).
2. The UK payments to the fourth resource in 1989 and VAT own resources in 1990 exclude contributions to the monetary reserve.
3. The figures for contributions of agricultural and sugar levies and customs duties in 1990 are based on projections underlying the 1989 autumn statement. They represent a more up-to-date forecast than the contribution figures in the 1990 budget as contained in Table 2.
4. Because of rounding the column totals do not necessarily equal the sum on the individual items.
5. The figures for VAT own resource and fourth resource payments include adjustment for previous years.

Source: *Statement on the 1990 Community Budget* CM 1059 HMSO London 1990 page 12

(a) Suggest reasons for the rising level of contributions to the budget via customs duties in recent years.

(b) Analyse why the UK does so badly in net terms from the budget.

(c) Does the above picture indicate that membership of the EC is *not* a good thing?

Exercise 5

Essay questions

1. Why has the EC had such difficulty in trying to control the level of agricultural spending?

2. Why is it difficult to fully assess the benefits of the completion of the Single European Market?

3. 'The EC is an ideal organisation to deal with those policy areas where nation states find that they are interdependent.' Discuss.

Exercise 6

Group discussion

The EEC's internal market has been slower to develop than many people hoped, because of the existence of non-tariff barriers to trade. Although these barriers preserve the interest of national producers who wish for protection from imports, they do reduce the opportunities for exporters.

Divide into two groups, one representing the interest of those who wish to protect the domestic market. The other group should represent the interest of exporters to the EEC countries.

The protectionist group should prepare arguments in favour of:

(a) national health regulations;

(b) increased border vigilance;

(c) the national choice of indirect tax rates.

The exporters should attempt to show how the above really act as non-tariff barriers and reduce the economic welfare.

ANSWERS

Exercise 1

Mix and match A. 7   B. 1   C. 8   D. 4   E. 3   F. 2   G. 5   H. 6

Exercise 2

Practical exercise

(a) See Fig. 30.1   (b) 35

(c) 25 domestic, 20 imported   (d) 15 domestic, 40 imported

(e) Increased consumption KLC, trade creation DEF as shown in Fig. 30.1

(f) ECHG   (g) No, KLC + DEF is smaller than ECGH

Fig. 30.1

(a)

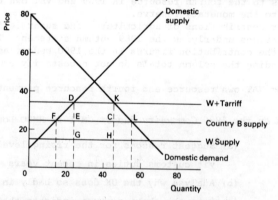

Exercise 4

Data response

(a) The major reasons could be either an increase in the tariff levels or increased levels of imports coming into the UK from outside the EC. It was in fact the second reason, because the EC has generally tried to reduce tariff levels on most areas of imports.

(b) Because the UK has a small agricultural sector, it is unable to benefit fully from the EC's spending in that area, which amounts to about two thirds of overall spending. Other areas of funding such as regional assistance are simply not large enough to compensate.

(c) The benefits from membership could come about because of the dynamic effect that creating trade brings to the UK economy.

31 Economic inequality

Policy makers frequently face difficult choices in trying to increase
social welfare. Perhaps the most fundamental one is deciding the degree
to which economic efficiency should be sacrificed in order to achieve a
socially desirable distribution of income. In order to do this, it is
important to investigate the extent of inequalities of income in a
society, and the success that government have had in their attempts to
redistribute it.

Measuring the distribution of income

There are problems in saying precisely what constitutes income, although
this should not cause too many problems if a sufficiently wide definition
is adopted. Earned income is the most important component making up
78 per cent in 1977. There is, however, little precision in this figure
and any other in the area, given that incomes tend to be under-reported
to the tax men, and tax returns do not tell us much about individual
incomes. We do know, however, that income inequality does exist and that
the degree of inequality changes over a period of time. This inequality
can be analysed by looking at the ratio of the shares of income received
by the top and bottom 20 per cent of the population and ascertaining the
extent to which they deviate from complete equality over a period of
time. Alternatively, it is possible to illustrate inequality graphically
by use of Lorenz curves and to show how distributions change before and
after tax, and over a time period.

International comparison

International comparisons of income inequality are difficult to make
because the sources of data are often not comparable and, in any case,
influences such as the variability of exchange rates distort them. When
capitalist economies are compared, we find that the degree of inequality
varies, with countries like Australia being more equal than the USA. It
is to be expected that socialist countries have more equal distributions,
but in less developed countries the degree of inequality is markedly
greater. The problem is that in these countries, the quality of data is
often particularly poor. Many people either live outside the market
economy or just on its fringes.

Causes of economic inequality

The state is able to influence the degree of inequality by the use of the
taxation system and public spending. These instruments help counteract
the forces in society which contribute towards income inequality. A
major cause of inequality is the unequal distribution of wealth. The
measurement of wealth is not an easy task, but it is clear that in the UK

185

Economic inequality

it is less evenly distributed than income. Owning wealth not only
provides status and security but is a means of generating income. Other
causes of income inequality are the degree of natural ability which
individuals possess, their training and life opportunities and the extent
to which they are protected by institutions such as trade unions.

EXERCISES

Exercise 1

Mix and match

A. Pareto's law

B. Direct benefit in kind

C. Line of complete equality

D. Lorenz curve

E. Fiscal drag

F. Transfer payments

1. A graphical representation of the distribution of
   personal incomes.

2. The effect that inflation has in increasing money
   incomes, so bringing more people into the tax
   net.

3. A theory which states that the number of income
   recipients earning at least a given level of
   income will tend to fall by a fixed percentage as
   that given level of income, rises by a fixed
   percentage.

4. A redistribution of income from tax payers to
   receivers.

5. Services available to individuals free and at a
   much reduced cost, for example the National
   Health Service, education, and school meals.

6. Where the percentage of income received is
   exactly equal to the percentage of income
   recipients.

Exercise 2

Practical exercise Using the data in Table 31.1, which relates to UK personal incomes, you
are required to construct Lorenz curves to show the degree of inequality
in both pre-tax and post-tax income distributions. Briefly comment on
the limitations of the Lorenz curve approach to illustrating the degree
of inequality in income or wealth distributions.

Economic inequality

Table 31.1 1985/86 Annual income survey

Lower limit of range of income	1985/85 Annual Survey			
	Number of incomes	Total income before tax	Tax	Total income after tax
All incomes	21,900	209,000	40,500	168,000
Income before tax £				
2,200	672	1,580	18	1,560
2,500	1,070	2,920	95	2,820
3,000	969	3,140	193	2,950
3,500	1,020	3,810	294	3,520
4,000	1,100	4,660	470	4,190
4,500	1,040	4,930	582	4,350
5,000	1,080	5,670	731	4,930
5,500	1,010	5,790	784	5,010
6,000	1,840	11,900	1,850	10,100
7,000	1,710	12,800	2,180	10,600
8,000	3,010	27,000	4,810	22,200
10,000	2,100	22,900	4,270	18,600
12,000	2,130	28,500	5,520	23,000
15,000	1,770	30,200	6,250	24,000
20,000	975	23,200	5,460	17,700
30,000	307	11,300	3,410	
50,000	87	5,650	2,180	3,460
100,000 and over	17	2,810	1,390	1,430

Source: *Annual Abstract of Statistics*, Central Statistical Office, 1989

Exercise 3

Short-answer questions

1. What are the deficiencies associated with the Survey of Personal Income?

2. What are the deficiencies associated with the Family Expenditure Survey?

3. How do tax allowances and relief tend to reduce the progressive nature of the tax system?

4. How does the phenomenon of fiscal drag influence the degree of income inequality in society?

Exercise 4

Data response

With reference to Table 30.2 answer the following questions:

(a) What percentage of personal wealth is held by:

    i) the least wealthy 75 per cent,

    ii) the least wealthy 50 per cent,

    iii) the most wealthy 10 per cent,

    of the UK population in 1986?

Economic inequality

(b) By comparing the UK personal wealth distributions, shown in Table 30.2, determine the year in which wealth is least unequally distributed. How confident can you be in drawing your conclusion?

(c) What factors would have the greatest impact on distribution of personal wealth?

Table 31.2 Personal wealth: Distribution among the adult population of marketable wealth series (C)

Percentages

	1966	1971	1976	1981	1984	1985	1986[1]	1987[1]
Concentration of wealth among adult population								
Percentage of wealth owned by:								
Most wealthy 1 per cent of adult population	33	31	24	21	18	18	18	18
Most wealthy 2 per cent of adult population	42	39	32	27	24	24	24	24
Most wealthy 5 per cent of adult population	56	52	45	40	37	37	36	36
Most wealthy 10 per cent of adult population	69	65	60	54	51	52	50	50
Most wealthy 25 per cent of adult population	87	86	84	77	75	76	75	74
Most wealthy 50 per cent of adult population	97	97	95	94	92	92	92	93
Distribution of adult population by individual net wealth								
Percentage of population with								

Over (£)	Not over (£)								
	5,000	91	85	69	49	42	43	41	40
5,000	15,000	7	12	23	27	22	20	18	15
15,000	50,000	1.7	2.7	6.8	20	27	27	30	30
50,000	100,000	0.4	0.4	0.9	3.1	6.1	7.5	8.7	11
100,000		-	0.3	0.4	1.2	2.2	3.1	3.1	4.3

	1966	1971	1976	1981	1984	1985	1986	1987
Total adult population (thousands)	30,228	39,809	40,496	41,868	42,765	43,054	43,322	43,433
Gini coefficient (Series C)	81	80	76	70	67	67	66	66

[1] Provisional

Source: *Inland Revenue Statistics*, 1989

Exercise 5

Essay questions

1. Analyse the problems associated with using the taxation system to overcome inequalities in the distribution of personal wealth.

2. 'Economic inequality is inevitable within any market economy.' Discuss.

Economic inequality

3. Outline the problems of trying to estimate the distribution of income and wealth within society.

Exercise 6

Group discussion

A political party decides it wishes to reduce the degree of income inequality in society. Discuss how the following problems might be overcome:

Fringe benefits

Incentive to work

Inequality of opportunity

Lack of natural ability

Inequality of wealth

Try to devise a strategy which takes account of these difficulties.

ANSWERS

Exercise 1

Mix and match

A. 3   D. 1
B. 5   E. 2
C. 6   F. 4

Exercise 2

Practical exercise

One limitation of the Lorenz curve approach to illustrating the degree of inequality in income or wealth distributions is that we cannot say how much more unequal one distribution is than another from a mere comparison of curves. Another limitation is that Lorenz curves may cross so that, in the absence of further information, it is difficult to say which income or wealth distribution shows the greatest degree of inequality. Thirdly, we may have insufficient data points to fairly assess the degree of inequality in a particular distribution; a criticism which especially applies to wealth distributions.

In practice, Gini coefficients are often calculated in conjunction with Lorenz curve data and these statistics allow objective comparisons to be made between various distributions regarding the degree of inequality.

Economic inequality

Data required to construct Lorenz curves is shown in the table below.

Income Before Tax (£)	Cumulative % of Income Cases	Cumulative % of Pre-Tax Income	Cumulative % of after-tax Income
2,200	3,06	0.76	0.92
2,500	7.95	2.16	2.6
3,000	12.37	3.66	4.35
3,500	17.03	5.48	6.44
4,000	22.05	7.72	8.93
4,500	26.8	10.08	11.52
5,000	31.73	12.79	14.45
5,500	36.34	15.57	17.42
6,000	44.74	21.26	23.42
7,000	52.54	27.40	29.72
8,000	66.28	40.33	42.91
10,000	75.87	51.3	53.96
12,000	85.59	64.95	68.62
15,000	93.67	79.42	81.87
20,000	98.12	90.53	92.39
30,000	99.52	95.95	97.09
50,000	99.92	98.75	99.15
100,000 and over	100	100	100

Exercise 4

Data response

(a) i) The least wealthy 75 per cent of the UK adult population held 15 per cent of total personal wealth in 1986.

ii) The least wealthy 50 per cent of the UK adult population held 8 per cent of total personal wealth in 1986.

iii) The most wealthy 10 per cent of the UK adult population held 50 per cent of total personal wealth in 1986.

(b) According to Gini coefficients (and the Lorenz curves, which can be constructed from the data provided) personal wealth is least unequally distributed in 1986/7. In fact, the distributions are very similar in 1984 and 1985 and it would be useful to have more data relating to these years. However, the Gini coefficients for 1984-1987 are decidedly lower than the coefficient for earlier years so that despite the poor quality and unreliability of some of the personal wealth data we can be reasonably confident in concluding that personal wealth was less unequally distributed in 1984-1987 than in earlier years.

NB. Figures do not take account of inflation.

(c) Taxation, tax allowances, welfare benefits, employment, inflation.

Exercise 5

Essay questions   1.

* The problem of taxing wealth is that it is often difficult to decide precisely what it is.
* Wealth taxes can alter the basis of the economic system if they discourage accumulation of assets.
* The wealthy may be able to realise more in the way of income.
* There may well be a problem of excessive transfers of wealth either to nominees or overseas.

32 Multiple-choice: Test 1 microeconomics

This self-assessment test is to be completed after studying Chapters 1 to 16.

QUESTIONS

1.

Fig. 32.1

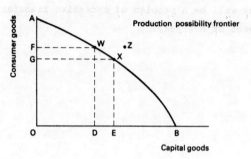

If a country was producing at point W it could increase output of capital goods from OD to OE by reducing output of consumer goods by:

(a) OG

(b) AF

(c) AG

(d) FG

2. A firm has a fixed amount of land and capital and increases production by employing labour according to the following schedule:

Labour	Output
1	15
2	32
3	51
4	67
5	71
6	70

The law of diminishing returns begins to operate:

(a) after 3 units of labour are employed

(b) after 4 units of labour are employed

(c) after 5 units of labour are employed

(d) after 6 units of labour are employed

3. In Fig. 32.2, which of the following could have moved the budget line from AB to AC:

   (a)   a decrease in the consumer's income

   (b)   an increase in the consumer's income

   (c)   a decrease in the price of apples

   (d)   an increase in the price of oranges

Fig. 32.2

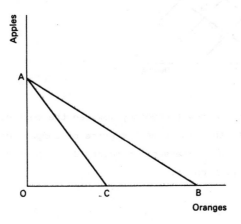

4. In the market situation shown in Fig. 32.3 where the government has imposed a maximum price below the equilibrium price what is likely to happen:

   (a)   supply expanding from 0Q to 0Z

   (b)   growth of a 'black market'

   (c)   a decrease in demand

   (d)   government purchases quantity WX from abroad and sells to home customers

Fig. 32.3

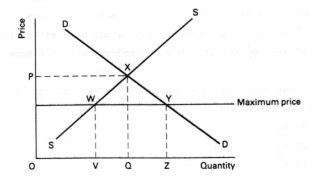

5. The curves SS and DD in Fig. 32.4 represent the initial supply and
    demand curves for compact discs and $\underline{X}$ the initial equilibrium:

Fig. 32.4

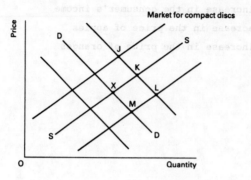

Market for compact discs

If, over time, new technology lowered the cost of producing compact
discs and at the same time the price of compact disc players fell,
which of the new intersection points J, K, L or M would represent the
new equilibrium point:

(a) J

(b) K

(c) L

(d) M

6. Countries A and B produce meat and fish only. They devote the same
    units of input to each good and produce the following outputs per
    month:

	Meat (kg)	Fish (kg)
Country A	7,500	1,500
Country B	5,000	1,000

However, in these circumstances specialisation and trade would not
take place because:

(a) transport costs would outweigh the benefits to be gained

(b) whatever the terms of trade only one country would benefit

(c) country A can produce both goods more efficiently

(d) the opportunity cost of production is the same in each country

7. To maximise short-run profit, the firm in Fig. 32.5 must produce the
    output level:

(a) X_3

(b) X_1

(c) X_4

(d) X_2

Fig. 32.5

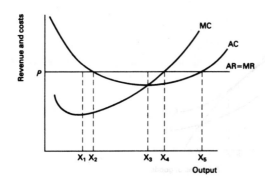

8. If the firm in Fig. 32.6 aims to maximise profit, then it will expect to make supernormal profit equal to the rectangle:

    (a) CEHF

    (b) CDGF

    (c) ABKJ

    (d) ABGF

Fig. 32.6

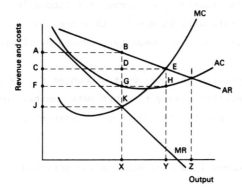

9. Figure 32.7 shows a range of choices between public and private provision of goods. Which point represents a Pareto optimal allocation of resources towards the public sector: a, b, c or d?

Fig. 32.7

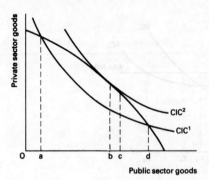

10. A single factory operating on an industrial estate is in the position where its social costs of production are not equal to its private costs. Which one of the following will increase welfare?
    (a) a tax when social costs are smaller than private costs
    (b) a tax on other factories on the estate
    (c) a subsidy to other factories when the social costs of the enterprise are smaller than its private costs
    (d) a tax when social costs are greater than private costs

11. An industry's elasticity of demand for labour in relation to changes in the wage rate will be greater than one if:
    (a) the demand for the commodity produced by the industry is inelastic
    (b) the proportion of total cost accounted for by labour is small
    (c) it is relatively easy to substitute capital for labour
    (d) the union bargaining position for workers in the industry is weak

12. Table 32.1 gives financial data on the performance of four companies.
Table 32.1

	company 1	company 2	company 3	company 4
Sales (£m.)	50	0.2	700	10
Profit margin on sales (%)	12.5	15	15	17.5
Capital employed (£m.)	125	1.5	1,000	45

Which of the companies had the highest return on capital employed.
    (a) company 1
    (b) company 2

(c)   company 3

(d)   company 4

In the questions below one or more options are correct. In each case select the appropriate letter from the following table:

(a)	(b)	(c)	(d)
1, 2 & 3	1 & 2	2 & 3	1
all	are	are	only
correct	correct	correct	correct

13. The demand for loanable funds may be relatively interest-inelastic if:

    (1) firms are likely to adjust their investment plans in response to the rate of change of national income

    (2) investment budgets are determined over a long time horizon

    (3) firms are experiencing liquidity problems

14. Which of the following statements relating to the demand for public and private goods is correct?

    (1) the existence of free riders makes it difficult to estimate the market demand for public goods

    (2) the market demand curve for private goods is the summation of individual demand curves

    (3) the demand curve for a public good must be summed vertically

15. Which of the following can be claimed as the benefits of a competition policy?

    (1) a widening of consumer choice

    (2) a better system of information about prices

    (3) improved economic efficiency

ANSWERS

1(d)   2(a)   3(d)   4(b)   5(c)   6(d)   7(c)   8(d)   9(b)

10(d) 11(c) 12(c) 13(a) 14(a) 15(a)

33 Multiple-choice: Test 2 macroeconomics

This self-assessment test is to be completed after studying Chapters 17 to 30.

QUESTIONS

1. The capital stock of a country at the beginning of 1985 was valued at £25,000m. At the end of that year it was valued at £30,000m. Capital consumption during the year was estimated to be £2,500m. What was the percentage change in the net capital stock?

   (a) 10%

   (b) 20%

   (c) 5%

   (d) 30%

2. Which of the following combinations of injections and withdrawals could not result in equilibrium being established?

   (a) savings exceed investments, tax exceeds government expenditure, exports exceed imports

   (b) savings less than investments, tax less than government expenditure, exports equal imports

   (c) savings exceed investments, tax less than government expenditure, exports equal imports

   (d) savings equal investments, tax less than government expenditure, imports exceed exports

   In questions 3, 4 and 5 below, one or more of the options is correct. In each case select the appropriate letter from the following table:

(a)	(b)	(c)	(d)
1, 2, 3	1, 2	2, 3	1
all correct	only correct	only correct	only correct

3. In a closed economy with no government sector, $C = 50 + bY$ and the multiplier is 5. It may be inferred that:

   (1) $C = 50 + 0.8Y$

   (2) $S = -50 + 0.2Y$

   (3) $C = 50 + 0.2Y$

4. In an economy with no foreign trade and public sector, if $C = 3,000 + 0.5Y$ it follows that:

   (1) investment equals half the national income

   (2) the value of the multiplier is 2

   (3) savings and investment are equal at equilibrium

198

5. Policy measures appropriate to alleviate the poverty trap would be:

    (1) to increase unemployment benefit

    (2) to increase personal allowances

    (3) to increase personal tax thresholds

6. What would be the effects on personal taxation of negative inflation in assuming no changes in pre-tax money incomes, tax rates or allowances?

    (a) the real value of personal tax allowances should fall

    (b) the real value of personal taxes would rise

    (c) there would be an increase in the proportion of taxpayers in the higher tax rates

    (d) there would be a decrease in the proportion of taxpayers under the lowest tax threshold

7. Which of the following developments is most likely to have an adverse effect on the UK balance of payments on current account?

    (a) a relative increase in foreign interest rates

    (b) a decrease in tourism abroad by British residents

    (c) tariffs imposed by the UK government on Japanese imports into the UK

    (d) abolition of tax rebates to British exporters

8. Which of the following combinations of elasticities of demand for exports and imports is least likely to allow a devaluation of a currency to improve that country's balance of payments?

	Import elasticity of demand	Export elasticity of demand
(a)	0.7	0.9
(b)	1.2	0.3
(c)	0.2	0.1
(d)	0.4	0.7

9. A British manufacturer sells 200 units per week in France at a sterling price of £5 per unit. The present rate of exchange is £1 = 10FF. If the elasticity of demand for the product in France is 1.5, what would be the expected level of sales if the exchange rate changed to £1 = 12FF?

    (a) 140 units per week

    (b) 260 units per week

    (c) 200 units per week

    (d) 160 units per week

10. In relation to the lending activities of the commercial banks, which of the following would reduce the size of the credit multiplier?

   (a) a reduction in the public's demand for cash

   (b) an improvement in the country's balance of payments

   (c) the decision by banks to reduce the ratio of cash reserves to deposits on prudential grounds

   (d) a requirement that banks should hold a higher proportion of their eligible liabilities in the form of non-operational deposits with the Bank of England

11. The income velocity of circulation of £M3 might fall while the velocity of M1 rises because:

   (a) being different definitions of money, the respective velocities will always move in different directions

   (b) unless this is the case the national income could not rise

   (c) following an increase in the general level of interest rates, the interest differential between bank time deposits and building society deposits moves in favour of the former

   (d) of a reduction in households' aggregate holdings of interest-bearing money in favour of increased holdings of building society deposits

12. Monetarists believe that there is a lag of up to 2 years before prices fully adjust to money supply changes because:

   (a) output must always adjust in the first instance

   (b) imperfect market information, market imperfections, uncertainty and inertia characterise most economies

   (c) in the first instance the public will not wish to change their spending on goods and services

   (d) interest rates must change before there can be any significant change in consumer spending and investment

13. In which of the following situations would fiscal policy be most effective?

   (a) both investment and the demand for money are interest-inelastic

   (b) both investment and the demand for money are interest-elastic

   (c) investment is interest-inelastic and the demand for money is interest-elastic

   (d) investment is interest-elastic and the demand for money is interest-inelastic

14. In which of the following situations would monetary policy be most effective?

    (a) investment is interest-inelastic and the demand for money is interest-elastic

    (b) the demand for money is interest-inelastic and investment is interest-elastic.

    (c) both the demand for money and investment are interest-elastic.

    (d) both investment and the demand for money are interest-inelastic.

15. If the percentage increase in the average price of alcoholic drinks rises from 6 per cent in one year to 9 per cent in the next, while the percentage increase in the average price of all other goods falls from 6 to 5 per cent, then UK inflation, as measured by the retail price index, would:

    (a) fall

    (b) remain unchanged

    (c) rise

    (d) rise or remain unchanged

ANSWERS

1(a) 2(b) 3(b) 4(c) 5(c) 6(b) 7(d) 8(c)

9(a) 10(d) 11(c) 12(b) 13(c) 14(b) 15(a)